C000297147

UNDERSTANDING SUPPORT NETWORKS AND COMMUNITY CARE

The Joseph Rowntree Foundation has supported this project as part of its programme of research and innovative development projects, which it hopes will be of value to policy makers and practitioners. The facts presented and views expressed in this manuscript, however, are those of the author and not necessarily those of the Foundation.

Understanding Support Networks and Community Care

Network assessment for elderly people

G. CLARE WENGER
Centre for Social Policy Research and Development
University of Wales Bangor

Avebury

Aldershot · Brookfield USA · Hong Kong · Singapore · Sydney

Published by
Avebury
Ashgate Publishing Limited
Gower House
Croft Road
Aldershot
Hants GU11 3HR
England

Ashgate Publishing Company
Old Post Road
Brookfield
Vermont 05036
USA

British Library Cataloguing in Publication Data

Wenger, G. Clare
    Understanding Support Networks and Community
    Care: Network Assessment for Elderly People —
    (Avebury Studies of Care in the Community)
    I. Title II. Series
    362.6

ISBN 1 85628 667 3

Printed and Bound in Great Britain by
Athenaeum Press Ltd, Newcastle upon Tyne.

Contents

Figures and tables

Foreword

Clare Wenger's analysis of support networks has always impressed me. In this short text she brings alive her academic analysis by making it available to professionals to use in a simple and sympathetic way. The user-friendly PANT instrument, based on 8 essential questions, is a must for every community-based worker to use in assessing clients' support networks. This book provides an exhilarating introduction to the process.

John Bond
Reader in Social Gerontology
University of Newcastle upon Tyne

Preface

Research on support networks started in Bangor in 1978. The first survey in 1979 made it possible to look at networks as entities and as the work progressed a network typology was developed. This was the product of many years of detailed research with many elderly people who willingly gave of their time.

Subsequent research demonstrated that network type was related to many areas of behaviour and that it might prove to be possible to develop an assessment instrument which would enable community care workers to predict responses of elderly people living in the community to the problems which befall them, the services that would be most appropriate and how they would respond to service interventions.

This book presents an account of the development of such an instrument through work with several community care teams. It looks at the process of introducing change into practice and at the relationships between network type and problems and solutions. It is based on the work of the participating teams and on real cases that they encountered during the study period.

The aim of the book is to present the support network typology to a wider audience, to indicate how network type can be used in practice and to suggest the identification of support network type as a screening tool and a quick, reliable assessment of the social context of elderly people seeking formal help.

It is my hope that managers and practitioners providing services for elderly people will find the network typology to be a useful and helpful assessment tool.

G. Clare Wenger
Gwaenysgor, Clwyd
24th November, 1993

Acknowledgements

The work presented in this book has been made possible by funding from the Department of Health (Welsh Office) and the Joseph Rowntree Foundation. This support has been much appreciated.

The generous participation and support received from the collaborating community care teams is also recognised. The project could not have been conducted without members of:

The Dales Team, Cumbria Social Services Department, Egremont.

The High Furness Team, Cumbria Social Services Department, Ulverston.

The Coventry Community Support Team (Elderly Health), Coventry Health Authority and SSD.

Aberconwy Elderly and Physically Handicapped Team, Gwynedd Social Services Department, Llandudno.

Arfon Elderly and Physically Handicapped Team, Gwynedd Social Services Department, Caernarfon.

The Llandudno Hospital Social Work Team, Gwynedd Social Services Department.

In addition, I wish to express my thanks to Kerry Caldock who handled much of the coding of Phase 1 data and provided helpful comments on earlier drafts of the MS; Said Shahtahmasebi who was responsible for data handling and processing and Barbro Das-Gupta who prepared the manuscript.

Part I
BACKGROUND

1 Support network variation

This book is based on the recognition that different types of informal support networks exist, which have different capacities for care and thus implications for formal care provision in the community. It describes work on the development of an instrument for the practitioner assessment of support network type, discusses some of the problems of introducing change into practice and shows how network type interacts with presenting problems and interventions.

Earlier work on the support networks of elderly people living in the community identified five different types of networks (Wenger 1989). Support network type has been shown to be related to the use of statutory domiciliary services at high levels of statistical significance and the distribution of network types has been found to be related to community or neighbourhood characteristics/type (Wenger and Shahtahmasebi 1990). Thus, it is suggested, the distribution of network types in any area has significant implications for care in the community.

In the context of recent government reports and new legislation implemented on 1st April 1993, (Griffiths 1988, DoH 1989, 1990 W.O. 1991) the emphasis on community care has grown. In the course of the next one or two years structural changes are envisaged which are intended to result in a shift of resources from institutional provision to the enhancement of domiciliary support. Central to much of the discussion of these changes has been the need for adequate assessment of potential clients of domiciliary and residential services.

While the subject of community care has been popular for over 30 years (Townsend 1962) its image has shifted over the years away from that of the caring community to the recognition that most dependent people cared for in the community are tended by spouses or female members of the immediate family (Qureshi and Walker 1989; Clifford 1990). Earlier work by the author

3

has identified a hierarchy of normative expectations of support depending on the nature of the relationship between network members (Wenger 1987) and Qureshi and Walker (1989) have identified a parallel hierarchy of carers, which has high predictive reliability.

The hierarchies referred to above show that receipt of necessary care in the face of dependency depends on the local availability of network members for whom normative expectations of care exist, namely spouses, adult children or, in a minority of cases, sisters. The network typology described below makes it clear that for substantial numbers of elderly people such relationships do not exist. In these cases personal care and services will be sought from the statutory services.

The support network typology is based on the following factors:

1 proximity of close kin;
2 the proportions of family, friends and neighbours involved; and
3 the levels of interaction between the old person and their family, friends, neighbours and community groups.

The network types are named on the basis of the old person's relationship to the support network. Network type has been found to be statistically correlated with all demographic variables except gender (Wenger and Shahtahmasebi 1989). The five types are summarised as follows:

(i) The family dependent support network has primary focus on nearby kin ties, close family relationships and few peripheral friends and neighbours. It is often based on a shared household with adult children, sister(s) or brother(s), or very near separate households. Most commonly the old person relies primarily on a daughter.

Statistically, persons with this network type are more likely than other types (p=.0000): to be over 80; widowed; to have daughters; to be living with or within 5 miles of relatives, especially children; to have moved short distances after retirement, and to have daily contact with relatives, mainly in the same household. Networks are more likely than other types to be small (1-4).

An elderly person with this type of network would be inclined to describe their situation as follows: "I'm very lucky to have my family near me. They'll take care of me if necessary."

(ii) The locally integrated support network includes close relationships with local family, friends and neighbours. Many friends are also neighbours. This network is usually based on long term residence and active community involvement in the present or recent past.

4

Statistically, persons with this network type are more likely: to be under 80; to have lived in the same community since they were under 40; to have frequent contact with relatives (at least weekly); and to have children and/or siblings within 5 miles. Networks are more likely to be large (8+).

A person with this network type would probably tell you: "We all know each other round here and look out for each other. There's always someone popping in to see how I am."

(iii) The local self contained support network, typically has arms-length relationships or infrequent contact, with at least one relative living in the same or adjacent community, usually sibling, niece or nephew. Reliance is focused on neighbours but respondents with this type of network adopt a household focused lifestyle and community involvement, if any, tends to be very low key.

Statistically, persons with this network type are more likely: to be single; to be living alone; to be childless; and have no living siblings. Contact with relatives is likely to be either weekly or less than monthly and often perfunctory.

Old people with this network type would probably say: "I like to keep myself to myself, but I know the neighbours are there if I want them."

(iv) The wider community-focused support network is typified by active relationships with distant relatives, usually children and high salience of friends and few neighbours. The distinction between friends and neighbours is maintained. Respondents with this type of network are generally involved in community voluntary organisations. Absence of local kin is common. This network is commonly a middle-class adaptation.

Statistically, persons with this network type are more likely: to be married; to live with their spouse only; to be retirement migrants; to be living >50 miles from nearest child/sibling; and to have infrequent face-to-face contact with relatives. Networks are more likely to be large (8+).

An elderly person with this type of network would probably tell you: "Although all my family live away, I've got good friends nearby and they'd help me if I needed anything."

(v) The private restricted support network is associated with absence of local kin, other than in some cases a spouse; minimal contact with neighbours; no nearby local friends and lack of wider community contacts or involvements.

Statistically, persons with this network type are more likely to be married; to be childless or have their nearest child more than 50 miles away; live with their spouse only; to be migrants to the community after age 40;

5

to have no siblings or nearest living sibling more than 50 miles away; and to have infrequent face-to-face contact with relatives. Networks are mainly small (1- 4).

People with this type of network would be likely to say: "I don't really have much to do with the people round here but then I've always been independent/a bit of a loner."

In the earlier work on which this project was based, contacts with social workers, district nurses, home helps, meals on wheels (Wenger and Shahtahmasebi 1990) and members of the clergy were all significantly related to network type. These relationships reflect different levels of dependency and/or the availability of informal help. Those with private restricted support networks consistently receive proportionately more visits from social workers, meals on wheels, home helps and district nurses. Those with family dependent support networks also receive proportionately higher levels of visits from social workers, district nurses and members of the clergy, but low levels of meals on wheels and home helps. Respondents with local self-contained support networks receive higher levels of visits from social workers, district nurses, home helps and the clergy but only at advanced ages (80+), while those with locally integrated support networks receive a higher level of visits only from the clergy.

On the basis of these findings, it was hypothesised that:

1   Elderly people with different types of networks are likely to make different **levels** of demand on statutory services.

2   Clients with different types of networks are likely to make different **types** of demands on statutory and voluntary services

3   Knowledge and understanding of variation in support network type is likely to be a useful tool for community care practitioners at the level of the individual and the team.

This book describes and reports on the study set up to test these hypotheses. The next chapter (2) describes how the research was conducted. Part II of the book deals with the management of change and the responses of social workers. Chapter 3 discusses problems relating to proposed changes in individual practice and perspectives and Chapter 4 describes the impact of change at the policy and the organisational level.

Part III presents quantitative findings on support networks. Chapter 5 looks at the sample profile and network type distribution. Chapter 6 presents data showing the relationships between network types and presenting

6

problems. In Part IV the book moves on to consider qualitative data from meetings to discuss the application of the network typology to social work practice. The first chapter in this part (7) looks at the consequences of variation for practice and the subsequent chapter (8) discusses some of the successes and problems experienced in the use of network type in practice. The last chapter presents the author's conclusions and the training needs highlighted by the study.

2 The network assessment project

Objectives

The primary objective was to operationalize the support network typology for use by practitioners working in community care. The project was called the Practitioner Assessment of Network Type (abbreviated to PANT) project. To this end the intentions were:

1 To design and test an assessment instrument using pilot domiciliary support teams.

2 To develop and test a training package of practitioner intervention based on these assessments of network type.

3 In the light of 1 and 2, to produce an effective assessment instrument and training package with wide applicability for community care of the elderly.

4 To document the experience of participating pilot teams in a final report and to disseminate findings.

5 To write a handbook for practitioners providing care in the community entitled: **Support Networks of Elderly People: A Guide for Practitioners.**

The research methods

The project was conducted in two phases:

Phase 1 - Initial work involved discussion and negotiations with agencies and selected teams who had agreed to participate in adopting, testing and evaluation of the assessment instrument (see Appendix A - amended form) to determine support network type. Pilot teams then tested the instrument in the field over a period of 6-10 weeks as agreed in discussion with the practitioners involved.

In most cases initial meetings between the researcher and the participating teams took place after team leaders had discussed the project with team members and agreement on participation had been reached. In the case of one team, the researcher presented the project to the team. Participation in this case was agreed after the team had had a chance to discuss the presentation.

At the first, or briefing meetings, the researcher presented data from the earlier studies on the network typology, service and demographic correlates and its potential for practice. The aims of the project were discussed, Phase I was described in detail and Phase 2 outlined. The PANT assessment instrument was circulated and instructions for completing the form were explained.

For the purposes of the project, the PANT instrument was extended to include basic details of the team and practitioner, a minimal profile of the client (age, sex, marital status and household composition) and a description of: client identified needs; practitioner identified problems and needs and any relevant previous history (see Appendix A). At the feedback meeting, all forms completed during Phase 1 were collected and the data subsequently post-coded for computer analysis. A copy of the coding frame is attached as Appendix B.

At the end of the test period, feedback meetings were held with each team and their experience in using the instrument was discussed. All feedback meetings were taped with the agreement of the teams and subsequently transcribed. The meetings all followed a similar format. First, team members were asked about their experience in using the assessment forms in Phase 1, secondly, research plans for Phase 2 were presented and discussed and thirdly continued participation of teams in Phase 2 was negotiated. Some minor modifications of the instrument were made and due to the phased introduction of the teams into the project, successive teams were able to test subsequent versions of the instrument.

Analysis of Phase 1 data was fed back to the participating teams as part of Phase 2.

Phase 2 - The second phase of the work was initiated at the feedback meetings for Phase 1. Preparation for Phase 2 took the form of further discussion of the network typology and ways in which network type might be taken into account in planning interventions. Practitioners were then asked to use network assessments in the decision-making process of intervention and/ or the design of packages of care.

At the Phase 2 briefing meetings, practitioners were asked to complete 10 or more forms before the next meeting. Initially, it had been hoped that they would use the forms with all or most cases over a trial period but it became evident early on that practitioners wanted an agreed minimum number of completed forms. After agreeing ten each with the first team briefed, this became the precedent agreed with all teams. In the event, most teams had difficulty meeting this minimum over the 10-12 weeks period between the first and second meetings. In more than one case team leaders suggested postponing the feedback meetings because workers had not completed sufficient forms. In most cases, however, feedback meetings took place after the planned interval. All feedback meetings were held 4-6 months after the start of Phase 2. The data bank of Phase 1 data was augmented by additional data from Phase 2 returns.

Following feedback of data from Phase 1, the usefulness and validity of network type as a diagnostic and predictive tool were discussed. In both Phases 1 and 2, community care workers were asked to note problems which tended to be associated with particular types of support networks. In Phase 2 of the study, social workers were asked to use the network assessment instrument to determine support network type and then to try to take account of what they knew of the characteristics of the support network type in planning their work with that client. In feedback meetings after each phase, discussions with social workers were held in which specific cases, presenting problems and interventions were analysed. These meetings were recorded and subsequently transcribed. The qualitative data from those discussions is analysed in Part IV of this book.

Interim reports on each phase were circulated to participating teams, colleagues and scientific advisers for comment and subsequently modified or amended as appropriate. Most comments received from the teams confirmed or amplified the conclusions drawn in the draft reports.

On the basis of the experience of Phases 1 and 2 and the analysis of data from both phases, training materials and a handbook for practitioners have been prepared. However, a preliminary/bare bones draft of the handbook was made available to practitioners in Phase 2.

Part II
MANAGING CHANGE

Part II
MANAGING CHANGE

3 Working with community care teams

Selection/participation of teams

Teams became involved in the project as a result of dissemination of earlier findings on network variation and discussion of the planned project, through direct requests to the author, or as a result of requests from the author to management in social services departments.

Several approaches were made to the author from a number of professionals in the community care field. Three of the six participating teams entered the study through this route: two neighbourhood care teams (social services) in Cumbria and a multi-disciplinary mental health care team in Coventry. Three other teams joined the study as a result of approaches to managers in Gwynedd Social Services: two specialist area teams for the elderly and physically handicapped and one hospital social work team for elderly people.

The pilot teams do not represent a cross-section of community care practitioners, nor are the catchment areas representative of the UK range, since most are in rural or partially rural regions. The study, however, was not designed as a representative sample of practitioners and teams. The teams were selected as pilots in which the assessment instrument could be tested and the relationship between network type and presenting problems explored. However, as subsequent discussion will demonstrate, the nature of teams and the impact of external events on teams assumed a greater salience than anticipated.

Attitudes to participation in the project

Most teams seemed interested in the network typology and willing to participate in Phase 1, which was to test the instrument. There were observed differences in the levels of acceptance expressed about the project, ranging from whole-hearted enthusiasm to barely concealed scepticism. It is difficult to explain these differences and much may have been dependent on the way in which the project had been presented to the teams. Managers were on the whole the most enthusiastic, followed by team leaders. However, it was the grass roots workers who were being asked to complete the forms!

Impressionistically, it appeared that initial commitment to the project was greatest where team leaders had a good understanding of the typology and its potential applications, were themselves enthusiastic about participation and where teams were comfortable with the current political context within their agency. Those who were currently facing administrative reorganisation tended to see the project as introducing one more thing to worry about. This topic is explored in greater detail in Chapter 4.

One other point was raised subsequently by 2-3 teams. In the early phase of the project, some social workers were suspicious about the "labelling" implications of the typology. These initial misgivings were subsequently overcome, however, as it became clear that network type was intended to be primarily descriptive or diagnostic and that no intention existed to attempt to alter network type or to change lifestyles.

Completing forms

As mentioned in Chapter 2, participants in the study had pushed for a minimum number of forms to be completed in Phase 1. Few completed more than the agreed minimum number of 10. Numbers of forms completed per practitioner ranged from 1-12. Overall 306 forms were completed, a small number of which were void because not all items in the network assessment section had been completed.

Problems arising with completion of the assessment instrument were common to all teams and fall into three categories:

    (i)   Interpretation of questions
    (ii) Following instructions
    (iii) Interpretation of results.

(i) *Interpretation of questions:* Practitioners raised several questions about interpretation. They were uncertain whether spouses were relatives. It was decided to exclude spouses from the definition of relatives, since the presence or absence of a spouse is not part of network definition. The instrument was amended to make this explicit.

Difficulties also arose about whether or not a relative in the same household counted as the "nearest" relative or whether the question meant "nearest outside the household". The inclusion of household relatives is important for network type so the form was amended to make this explicit.

One practitioner had difficulty with question No. 7 "Do you attend religious meetings?" It was contended that if a member of the clergy visited the house to administer communion, this was a religious meeting. The intent of the question is to measure community involvement. It was decided to leave the question in its original form but to clarify this question in subsequent training sessions.

(ii) *Following instructions:* In presenting the assessment instrument, practitioners were shown the form which was then described to them and the instructions were read through once to familiarise them with the use of the instrument. From information given at the feedback meetings, it is clear that this is not sufficient introduction to the form. In subsequent work workers are asked to interview one another and to complete a sample form during the briefing meeting.

Two separate problems arose with regard to following instructions. Instructions on the assessment instrument ask practitioners to "circle the same code across all boxes on the same line". A common problem was that practitioners did not expect the same code to occur more than once on a line, which is the case. This meant that practitioner assessments tended to cluster in the left hand columns and network types on the right hand side of the page were under-represented.

The other common problem encountered was that instructions asked practitioners to "count circled codes for each network column and enter number at the bottom". The instrument used number codes and several workers added the codes which again gave inappropriate readings.

The instrument has again been modified taking account of these problems. Codes are now printed across the page on the same line as the values given in the left hand column, so that practitioners can see more clearly where the same value occurs more than once. Number codes have been changed to letter codes so that they cannot be added.

Because of the problems and inaccuracies introduced by practitioners in completing the assessment instrument, computer calculations of network type are used in the data analysis presented in this book.

17

(iii) *Interpretation of results:* In briefing sessions, practitioners were warned that borderline cases would occur, where the highest number occurred in more than one column. (For discussion, see Chapter 5.) However, many found this problematic and unsatisfactory. Some cases were inconclusive where the same number occurred more than twice. Some practitioners, particularly those less convinced at the outset, felt that these problems were indicative of the inadequacy of the instrument.

Borderline and inconclusive cases were discussed in feed-back meetings. In most early instances, problems were the result of inaccurate completion of the form. Remaining borderline cases could then be explained to practitioners. Since the network types are "ideal" types, not every network will fit clearly into a category in the real world. However, borderline cases may also reflect transitions or shifts from one type to another. It was noted that since shifts in network type occur predominantly as a result of growing dependency, it could be predicted that referrals to community care practitioners were more likely than others to have borderline networks, reflecting the fact that they are in flux.

The other problem of interpretation of results occurred where practitioners were unhappy about the outcome of the assessment. For example, someone they felt had a family dependent network came out as locally integrated. Usually on further exploration of the case, it became apparent that the practitioner's view was based on assumptions about the network types which were not part of their definition or assumptions about clients which proved to be inaccurate. In most instances, after further discussion workers were happy with the instrument assessment.

It was obvious that early problems associated with interpretation of outcomes of network type were due mainly to the limits of practitioners' familiarity with and understanding of the network typology. It was clear that the initial Phase 1 briefing and associated handouts had been insufficient background for workers to understand and work with network types. They needed more descriptive data of "ideal" types of networks and borderline types.

One of the planned outputs of the project was the production of the guide for use by practitioners. It had been imagined that this would be written towards the end of the project, incorporating the experience of the participating teams. Due to the difficulties being experienced by practitioners in Phase 1, it was decided to draft early chapters of the guide for use by participating teams as soon as possible in Phase 2. Due to the phasing of the study, some teams received their handbooks after Phase 2 had commenced while others were able to have them before Phase 1 had been completed.

One other problem occurred which resulted in a change of the instrument. Some of the social workers taking part felt that ethical considerations

18

demanded that clients should be told that the instrument was being used as part of a research project to determine network type. This was apparently well-received by the elderly people concerned who found it interesting and exciting to be part of a research study. However, the workers involved also felt that they should tell their clients the outcome and found that those whose networks were identified as Private Restricted were often upset by this.

To counter the above problem, it will be seen that Private Restricted networks are renamed as "Private" on the instrument. The way in which the form was used/introduced had been left to the workers concerned. Training sessions now suggest that the network questions be integrated into the assessment interview in as natural a way as possible, with no discussion of network type. (See further discussion below under Resistance to Change.)

Negotiating Phase 2

In Phase 2 it had been anticipated that practitioners would continue to use the assessment instrument, but would use the identification of network type as an indicator in planning interventions. This was introduced in initial briefing meetings and was then explored further in Phase 1 feedback meetings. It had been made clear to teams at the outset that continuance into Phase 2 would be negotiated at the end of Phase 1.

One team dropped out at this stage. The Coventry Mental Health Care team declined to continue with Phase 2. This team had included the network assessment instrument in a new assessment schedule. On the whole, very few problems were experienced with the assessment instrument. However, the question was raised as to whether the instrument was useful with psychiatric patients since all were subject to detailed assessment. There was some feeling that knowledge of network type was not necessary in the context of the detailed assessment. It was felt to be more useful as a screening instrument. Some useful insights into problems associated with different networks emerged during the meeting, however, which are discussed in Part IV of this book.

The Coventry team was also under stress at the time of their involvement. There was a certain amount of frustration because in addition to their usual work, which involved dealing with an average of 10 referrals per week, they were piloting a project on formal home based assessment, which had to be compared with hospital diagnostic assessments. The assessment document they were piloting already ran to 25 pages! Dropping the PANT instrument reduced the time of assessments so it was not unexpected when they declined Phase 2. This left only social services area teams in the study.

All other teams entered Phase 2.

19

Resistance to change

Some problems were experienced in attempts to change ways of working with which social workers were familiar. Reluctance to adopt new ways of conceptualising practice problems, which is what the use of network type implies, appeared to stem from two sources. In the first place, while practitioners were prepared to assist the researcher with the project, this was seen to be something extra, beyond their professional responsibilities; and, in the second place, the learning period needed to acquire familiarity with the network types was longer than had been anticipated. At the same time, it is possible that the magnitude of the task had been under-estimated. As one team leader commented in response to a draft report, what was sought was a "paradigm shift".

Changing the work patterns of social workers has been recognised by others as a difficult task (Goldberg 1965). Some practitioners were quite explicit about their offered level of involvement. For example, one social worker stressed:

> I'm quite prepared to fill in a few forms for you so long as you don't expect me to change the way I work.

Some saw the instrument in terms of "*not another form*". Others were less overt than the worker quoted above in their reluctance to change working styles:

> It really took too much time and what we gained from our interviewing anyway - We are perhaps set in a certain pattern with the interviewing. It is hard to make use of the actual instrument really - that's my regret.

When these sentiments were expressed in the context of earlier discussion of heavy workloads, it was difficult to feel that one was convincing or justified in arguing that it was change in ways of working that was exactly what was expected. The workers were after all participating in the project voluntarily.

The second problem which resulted in resistance to use of the network typology in practice has to be seen as due to project training inadequacies. One of the objectives of the project was to develop training packages for the introduction of the network typology into practice and it became obvious that a more intensive introduction to the various support network types and their implications would be necessary.

All team leaders commented on training needs in response to the draft report on Phase 2, commenting that understanding of the typology increased over the study period and that commitment increased with understanding. It

20

was suggested by one team leader that workers' prior training was likely to have stressed "social support" rather than "support networks" and that it was difficult for them to make the distinction between support and its source. The need for more comprehensive training was the dominant point made by all teams in their response to the draft interim report.

Some misunderstandings in the application of support network type occurred. In several instances, social workers thought that one goal was to change networks from more dependent, vulnerable types to more robust types of networks. This was not intended. What was intended was that community care workers would use the knowledge of a client's network type to design complementary, compatible packages of support or other interventions. Another concern which was expressed was that clients with networks with potential for informal care might be disadvantaged and services disproportionately focused on those with more vulnerable network types. Again, this had not been intended, although it has to be admitted that the typology could be used in this way.

It became clear that community care workers would need a better grounding in the attributes of the different network types; a better understanding of what could be expected of the networks in a range of situations; and considerably more discussion of the application of network types in practice. The learning curve became clear over the study period as social workers became more and more familiar with the nature of the different networks. However, team members said that they felt that they were only just beginning to feel comfortable with the typology at the end of Phase 2 of the project. The feedback meeting at this stage was only the third time that the teams involved had had discussions with the researcher on the nature of the different networks, although all workers had been provided with a draft of **Support Networks of Elderly People: A Guide for Practitioners** (Wenger 1994). It became clear that for the typology to be meaningful and useful, a more intensive training period paying detailed attention to applications will be required. (Further discussion of training implications can be found in Chapter 9.)

4 The political and organisational context

The work on the PANT project was started in 1990 in the context of the predicted shift to care in the community as urged by the **Griffiths Report** (1988) and the **Government White Paper, Caring for People** (DoH 1989). Most workers recognised that the focus of the study - variation in support networks - was particularly relevant to community care and the expected implementation of the White Paper recommendations in April 1991. However, as discussed in previous chapters, participation had to be negotiated with the teams and it became clear early in the project that two major factors unrelated to the nature and relevance of the study had a significant impact on both participation and the commitment and enthusiasm of the workers involved.

These two external intervening factors are not unrelated to each other and both relate to change in the organisational context in which workers found themselves. The first factor was organisational change and the second was the postponement of the implementation of the White Paper recommendations. While neither factor is directly connected with the use of support network type in practice, the effects of these changes are reported because they have significance for the introduction of innovation, which the use of the network typology represents. They are, therefore, relevant not only to the introduction of the use of the network typology but to the introduction of innovation generally.

There are indications that it could be change itself that makes the acceptance or integration of innovation difficult. It has been suggested that change in the organisational environment affects work behaviour and noted that change in one part of an organisation is likely to produce change in another (Handy 1985). What appears to have been happening in the departments associated with the study is that change instituted outside the organisation or at higher levels of the hierarchy had effects in the front line which had not or could not have been foreseen or were not recognised by management. The expressions of demoralisation and anxiety expressed to the researcher by front line workers were, however, more likely to be the result of how the changes were handled than the fact of change itself.

Hadley, Dale and Sills (1984), in their presentation of **"A Model for Change"**, suggest that for top-down change to be successful it is necessary: (1) to define goals collaboratively; (2) to legitimate risk taking and possible failures; (3) to provide resources to facilitate change; (4) to build in motivations for staff at all levels; (5) to share information with staff so that they feel part of the process; and (6) to integrate change into ongoing work. While not all of these aspects may be applicable in all instances of change, it is clear that most of them were not part of the organisational situation in which some front line workers participating in the PANT project found themselves. On the other hand, changes put in train to accommodate the recommendations of the White Paper appear to have been more integrated into the organisational structure and to have met numbers (1), (2), (5) and (6) above and to have met (4) for some members of staff. Reactions to the two changes were, therefore, different. Significantly, (3) the provision of resources to facilitate change, was missing in all instances.

As discussed above, continued participation into Phase 2 was renegotiated at the end of Phase 1. One of the participating teams dropped out at the end of Phase 1. Another team had withdrawn earlier before becoming actively involved in the study and it is suggested that this occurred in part because of the uncertainties engendered in that local authority by the structural reorganization of social services which was taking place at that time.

> We are reorganizing in order to meet the needs of care in the community ... so nobody has known what is happening for the last six months. It has been a nightmare really. ... There has been so much going on that nobody could make any decisions, because nobody knew what their position was going to be...... The whole thing has changed. ... They won't tell you what is going to happen, let alone ask you what you think should happen.

In Cumbria an earlier reorganization to neighbourhood based area teams had been accomplished prior to the start of the project. In this organisational context, teams expressed satisfaction in the fact that they were providing a superior service, despite the feeling of some workers that their workloads were heavier and that they had lost some of the emphasis on one-to-one working that they valued. That re-organisation appeared to have been handled well with consultation and cooperation with front line workers. Both teams in this authority agreed to participate in Phase 2 but during the second phase they were faced with new, unanticipated and sudden organisational change.

24

In this second case, the earlier reorganization, which had been introduced county-wide with no prior piloting, had proved to be more expensive than expected. Coupled with difficulties arising from the introduction of the community charge, the county found itself overspent and in danger of charge-capping. Area teams were immediately requested to limit the admission of new cases to only those which were urgent and to re-evaluate and review services for all current cases. Although the words "cut back" were not used, it was felt to be obvious that this was the expectation. Teams, which had been recently decentralised, were to be paired under team leaders. Team leaders all had to apply for these jobs, but the number of team leaders was to be halved. Other workers were concerned about the security of their own jobs and demoralisation and anxiety were reported to be high:

> We're feeling very low.
> Low! Low! We're fed-up to the back teeth!
> We have team meetings and we sit there and think, how are we going to cope with this latest blow that's come down from above!

> ... we are all unhappy now, not about neighbourhood care, but about what's happened because of lack of resources and all the other things happening at the moment.

> Suddenly it all blew up - we must cut, particularly in the home care services. ... every social worker had to review every case and cut the input. Every case, whether it was low priority, high priority or whatever, had to be looked at.... I have this awful feeling of constantly shifting sands .... you keep getting new directives.

In this climate of uncertainty, unpredictability and demoralisation, the workers found it difficult to maintain interest in the project, although they stated their determination to fulfil their commitment to the researcher. However, these events resulted in delays and reduced enthusiasm. A senior social worker commented, that the network typology had seemed tailor-made for their commitment to supporting elderly or physically disabled people in the community, but when the cuts came it seemed irrelevant because only those in the direst straits with no possible other source of help could receive any service at all. However, another social worker, speaking of their failure to use the network assessment instrument, said:

> What saddens me a little ... is that actually in this scenario, networking is even more important, but it's easy to forget to do it. ... I would like to put more emphasis on that.

Social workers in both authorities where their organisational context suffered flux during the period of the research, complained of two major problems which created demoralisation: (1) absence of consultation with or dissemination of information to front-line workers; and (2) insecurity or uncertainty about their own jobs. In most cases (2) was the result of (1). Under these conditions, it became difficult - and for some impossible - to think about further change, such as innovation in working practices which use of the network typology represented.

It seems to be significant that those social work teams not subject to organisational change during the study period (in one of the three authorities under discussion), appeared to be better able to take on board the new ways of working implicit in the use of support network type as a practice tool despite the fact that they had seemed the least enthusiastic at the outset. Also significant, is the fact that one team experiencing severe pressure subsequently requested the researcher to return to work on the application of network type in practice. While the situation had apparently not improved, it had settled down and work on this innovation was seen as a possible boost to morale as well as a potentially helpful tool. It seems clear then that it is not necessarily change per se which is resisted but the nature and amount of change.

During the study period, it was announced that the implementation of the White Paper recommendations was to be postponed until April 1993. In all the study authorities, planning had been focused on putting in place the necessary machinery for the shift in emphasis to community care. Despite the changes that this would entail, these appeared to be changes which - perhaps because of the widespread publicity which they had received - front line workers felt they understood. The go-stop nature of this shift was, therefore, experienced as disconcerting:

> ... that was going to change when the (recommendations of the) White Paper was going to come out and home care were going to be doing the packages, but as it is at the moment for the next two years, it doesn't look like that. We were going to be the ones who were actually going to do the assessments. ... Now, they are putting it on the shelf, they are finishing off the groups that they have got - the social work groups - and they are just putting it on the shelf apparently and waiting for two years until the money comes in. ..... Some of the home care organisers have been on these planning meetings, you know, putting their point forward and everything and they have got a lot done on these working parties. (Home care organiser, who had looked forward to the extension of her role.)

26

The thing that the government didn't seem to know was that obviously they'd (the local authority) appointed people in a lot of places ... I mean there's the cost of doing it but the cost of cancelling it is going to be pretty great as well. (Social worker)

I feel that they should just have gone ahead and done it. Obviously there isn't enough money to do all sorts of things but .. I think they were cruel in what they have done to us really. We had been emphasising to all our staff ... this is what we are going to be aiming at and this is going to change and then it's frozen. Then we will have to start all this enthusiasm again in two years.(Team leader)

... I think the morale of the staff, even ourselves, is confusion and worry. What is going to happen and when is it going to happen and when it does happen will it all change again? I think the morale is quite bad really at the moment." (Team leader)

... we are just going ahead with the inspectorate unit and the complaints unit ... So far as I understand the social care plans will be going to committee in October as originally agreed .... as far as possible we will try to implement the changes in terms of patch models and care managers and ... There was a survey, wasn't there, that found that only one local authority would not have been ready. We would have been ready. (Team leader)

While some workers expressed the view that April 1991 had been over-optimistic, most seemed to feel that commitment to the 1991 date had existed and that they would have preferred to have kept to that date. As it was, the postponement of the implementation left a vacuum and a feeling of being on hold. At the same time, the PANT project had been perceived to be particularly relevant to the post-Griffiths era and - although the effect was less obvious - the postponement also diluted enthusiasm for the project, which had been seen by many as an added preparation for the new focus of working. Both organisational and political changes in the research context, therefore, affected worker morale and commitment to the project.

Part III
SUPPORT NETWORKS, TEAMS AND USERS

5   Network distributions

While the primary object of Phase 1 was to test and modify the assessment instrument as needed, correlation of presenting problems with network type was also of interest. In this chapter, data from the completed network assessment forms, including supplementary questions, are analysed.

The composition of the participating practitioners is shown in Table 5.1 which shows the number of forms completed by different types of practitioners. The majority were social workers. Some subsequent analyses, therefore, are based on social worker cases, which made up more than 70% of the sample. The table also shows the proportions of old and new cases sampled and the source of the information collected.

The support network typology was developed based on the study of elderly people (65+) living in the community. However, some clients under the age of 65 have been included in the sample. Table 5.2 presents the client profile and shows that the overall age range was from 51 to 96, the modal age was 80-81 and the average age 78.5. The ages of clients cluster towards the 80+ end of the range with at least half being over 80. Approximately twice as many women as men occur as clients reflecting the population sex distribution for this age group. In other words, men are as likely to become clients as women. Practitioners rarely identify a couple as "the client".

Table 5.1
Sampling profile

	Study total
Number of forms completed	(306)
	%
By:	
Qualified social worker	33
Unqualified social worker	39
OT/OT assistant	7
Psychologist/Community psychiatric nurse	17
Home care organiser	2
Old cases	54
New cases	36
Not stated	10
Information from:	
Client	44
Some/all proxy	25
Not stated	31

Table 5.2
Client profile

	Total study (N = 306)
Age range	51-96
Average age	78.5
Mode	80-81

	%
Under 60	2
60-64	2
65-69	8
70-74	15
75-79	24
80-84 ⎫	27 ⎫
85-89 ⎬ 80+	14 ⎬ 49
90+ ⎭	8 ⎭

Male	29
Female	70
Couple	1

Married	28
Widowed	55
Single	15
Separated/Divorced	3

Lives alone	55
With spouse only	25
With younger relatives	11
With elderly relatives	3
Foster care	2
Residential care	3
Other	2

The support network typology, as described in Chapter 1, has five distinctive categories. In the real world, however, it is not always easy to determine which categories people fit into. Borderline cases must, therefore, be expected. Indeed, over time, shift in network type has been observed (Wenger 1990b). While not all borderline cases are the result of network shift, at a time when network shift is taking place, support networks are likely to include features of both the original and the destination network type. Shifts have been found to be mainly associated with the onset of mental illness or physical frailty. Therefore, the support networks of the clients of social services or medical patients are likely to include more than average numbers of borderline cases, as help is likely to be sought when the network is under stress and the nature of the network is in flux. Such periods of transition are likely to cause most stress for elderly people and those responsible for their care.

Network types discussed in this section are based on computer identification. Network type was identified for 289 cases. (Distributions of the eight questions used to identify network type are given in Appendix C). In 74% of cases support network type was identified unequivocally; in 23% of cases borderline network types were identified and for 3% identification was inconclusive.

Most shifts in network type are related to possibilities inherent in the existing network. Certain shifts are, therefore, predictable. Other shifts occur as a result of geographical relocation, which has the effect of disrupting the pre-existing network, inasmuch as the resulting network is no longer dependent on the original network. However, most shifts are of the first type. Not all shifts can or do occur. Five shifts are more likely to occur than others (Wenger 1990 b). Based on earlier work, those shifts most likely to occur are:

Locally integrated	$\longrightarrow$	Family dependent
Locally integrated	$\longrightarrow$	Local self-contained
Local self-contained	$\longrightarrow$	Private restricted
Wider community focused	$\longrightarrow$	Private restricted
Private restricted	$\longrightarrow$	Wider community focused

We can, therefore, predict that borderline cases are more likely to occur between the original and destination types represented by these predictable shifts. Table 5.3 shows the distribution of network types in the client/patient sample. It can be seen that two thirds, i.e. 44 (16%) of the 66 (23%) borderline cases involve borderlines that can be explained in terms of previously established predictable shifts.

One other borderline not previously identified as a possible shift occurred - between family dependent and private restricted support networks. This borderline accounted for 17 cases (6%). A possible explanation for the identification of this new borderline type lies in the fact that previous work was based on process over time rather than borderline cases. Since earlier network assessments had been done by assessors, best-fit network identifications were based on an overview of the subject's support network. Where most care was provided by a family member, networks were usually classified as family dependent. As noted above in family dependent support networks, care tends to devolve onto one family member with increased dependency. There are indications that this borderline is in fact associated with high levels of dependency. What the assessment instrument appears to be identifying here is a distinction between family care, where there is additional support to the elderly person and their carer, and those where there is not. This is an important addition to our understanding of support network types and alerts one to the importance of the recognition of differences within types. (Other identified borderlines not already discussed, involved one or two cases each.)

The most prevalent borderline case is that between locally integrated and family dependent network type, which accounted for 23 cases (8%). This reflects the availability of local involved family which is a common factor of locally integrated support networks. At higher levels of dependency, local family members assume primary responsibility for care and in the face of mental or other debilitating or terminal illness, contacts with friends and neighbours become less frequent or intense. For example, an active person living with an adult daughter may continue to participate in a range of reciprocal activities with other relatives, friends and neighbours but with increasing frailty, particularly if senile dementia occurs, will have less and less contact with those outside the family. Her daughter will take over all care and although the daughter may receive support from her locally integrated network, all her mother's needs are met within the family. The relatively large number of cases on this borderline suggests that it is at the point of shift to family dependency that help is sought from statutory services.

35

Table 5.3
Distribution of network type showing borderline cases (N=289)

	%	N
Family dependent	7	21
Family dependent/locally integrated	8	23
Locally integrated	21	60
Locally integrated/local self-contained	<1	3
Local self-contained	12	34
Local self-contained/Wider community focused	<1	2
Wider community focused	9	26
Wider community focused/private restricted	4	10
Private restricted	26	74
Private restricted/family dependent	6	17
Other borderlines:		
Local self-contained/private restricted	3	8
Locally integrated/wider community focused	<1	2
Locally integrated/private restricted	-	1
Inconclusive	3	8

*Starred borderlines represent predicted shifts

All previously identified shifts in network type were from more independent networks to more dependent network types with the exception of shifts from private restricted to wider community focused networks. However, because this project is concerned with clients/patients of statutory services, the assumption of increasing dependency is made since it is likely that an increased need for help is the trigger which brings elderly people to the attention of service providers. **For the purposes of analysis only**, it is, therefore, assumed that borderline cases reflect shifts towards more dependent network types. In order to reduce analytical categories, therefore, borderline cases are recoded/ aggregated to the assumed destination type of support network.

Table 5.4
Network distribution[1]

Network Type	All (N=279)
Family dependent	16
Locally integrated	23
Local self-contained	14
Wider community focused	7
Private restricted	41

[1]Omitting inconclusive assessments

In Table 5.5 and Figure 1 network distribution of cases from the PANT study is compared with the distribution for a rural North Wales population sample study and for a recent urban study conducted by the author in Liverpool. As can be seen clearly from Figure 1, the case load distribution is distinctively different from both population distributions. The differences between the two population samples reflect the higher proportion of incomers in the rural area (where 20% of the sample were retirement migrants) and the stability of the urban dwellers (where 96% had lived in the city for more than 30 years).

We have seen above that network type may shift over time. It might be anticipated, therefore, that distribution of network type would be related to age and this is in fact the case for the population samples. In the urban sample the proportion of private restricted support networks increased with age from 8% of those aged 65-69 to 29% of those aged 90+. In the rural sample those with family dependent support networks increased with age from 13% of those aged 65-69 to 24% of those aged 85-89. For the client sample, however, age was not significant; although the sa7mple was older there was no marked shift in distribution with age. The private restricted support network type was the dominant type in all age groups.

Table 5.5
Distribution of network types,
comparing a user sample with rural and urban population samples

Network type	PANT cases	Population samples	
		Rural N. Wales	Liverpool
	(N=306)	(N=240)	(N=4450)
Local family dependent	16	15	22
Locally integrated	21	42	42
Local self-contained	12	9	11
Wider community focused	8	20	4
Private restricted	40	7	15
Inconclusive	3	5	5
X^2 significance of age p =	N/S	.003	.0000

The major difference between the network distribution on case loads and the population distributions is the big difference in the proportions of private restricted networks. This type accounted for only 7% and 15% of networks in the population samples but 40%, i.e. approximately three times as many, in the case load sample. The private restricted network is a minority type amongst the general population so it can be seen that increases in the prevalence of such networks (due to increased migration; the mobility of labour; civil disruption or other reasons) have worrying implications for pressures on statutory services.

In contrast, fewer clients/patients have family dependent or locally integrated networks (and this difference increases when age is controlled for). Three fifths or more of elderly people in the general population live in one or other of these two most robust support networks compared with less than two-fifths of those on case-loads. As discussed elsewhere (Wenger and Shahtahmasebi 1990), it can be seen that those stronger network types make proportionately fewer demands on statutory services. **These findings support the first hypothesis: that elderly people with different types of networks are likely to make different levels of demand on statutory services.**

38

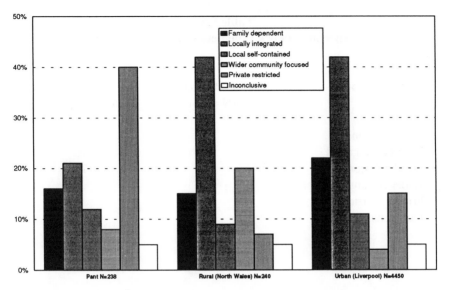

Figure 1
Distribution of network types*
Comparing a user sample with rural and urban population samples

Practitioners were asked whether cases were new or old. Some interesting differences in network type occur between old and new cases (p ≤.05). As Table 5.6 shows, while there is no difference between old and new cases in terms of wider community focused and private restricted support networks, differences are marked for family dependent and locally integrated networks. Old cases are predominantly related to private restricted and locally integrated support networks (62%), while new cases are predominantly from privately restricted and family dependent support networks (61%).

39

Table 5.6
Difference in network type between old and new cases

Network type	Old cases (N=157)	New cases (N=102)
Family dependent	12	23
Locally integrated	26	16
Local self-contained	16	11
Wider community focused	7	7
Private restricted	36	38
Inclonclusive	3	6
	100	100

There are proportionately twice as many new cases as old cases from family dependent networks, suggesting that elderly people with family dependent networks are more likely to be short-term service users. Qualitative data from the earlier work support this explanation. Help is sought late at high levels of dependency and is provided for a short period until death or admission to long-term care. Elderly people with family dependent networks are, therefore, likely to need high levels of intervention for short periods of time (Wenger 1990c, 1992).

In contrast, those with locally integrated support networks appear to be long-term service users. The proportion of this network type amongst service users most closely approximates their proportions in the population, but most were old cases. Qualitative data from earlier work (Wenger 1987, 1992) indicate that even where statutory help is provided, elderly people with locally integrated support networks continue to receive most help and support from informal sources. Since many live alone they are likely to qualify for help at lower levels of dependency and because they are involved in the community they are likely to be referred early by family, friends or neighbours at low levels of dependency. On the other hand, they are able to remain longer in the community at high levels of dependency than others for whom such informal help is not forthcoming.

40

Differences between network types in terms of statutory service use are predominantly reflected in the proportions using services as already discussed. However, some differences in presenting problems are also statistically significant. These are discussed in the next chapter.

6   Presenting problems

Presenting problems, recorded on the form as "client identified needs" or "practitioner identified needs and problems", were post-coded from the information given (see Appendix B). Only categories which were recorded in the 306 cases documented are included. While these data and the distribution of needs and problems are presented here, caution must be exercised in interpreting the data. The needs and problems shown were not used as a check list by practitioners and many clients inevitably suffered from problems other than those recorded as salient in the interview in question. The distribution is further affected by the distribution of professional affiliations. These must be regarded primarily as indicators. Our primary interest here is in differences between network types.

Some difficulties appeared to arise in terms of client identified needs. Although it was stressed at briefing meetings that this referred to the way in which **clients** expressed their problems, it was not always clear that practitioners were describing what their clients told them. Some practitioners had apparently made a conscious effort to elicit needs from the client but in a minority of cases one gained the impression that what was recorded was the **practitioner's** assessment of what the client's problems were.

Since most of the respondents were clients of social workers working in social work teams, social work figures are shown in a separate column in some of the following tables in order to control for differences in practitioners' professional background.

Client identified needs

Table 6.1 shows the percentages of clients in the whole sample compared with social workers' clients who identified themselves as having a particular need. Most clients mentioned more than one problem.

Table 6.1
Client identified needs (%)[1]

	Study total	Social workers/ Social work teams
	(N=306)	(N=214)
None recorded	15	7
Client says "None"	8	7
Poor health/limited mobility related[2]	**51**	**64**
Help with household tasks	35	46
Help with personal care	8	11
Problem with hearing/sight	5	7
Help with bathing/ADL/aids	4	2
Property modification	3	2
Linkage-transport/shopping	10	13
Emergency help/falls/alarms	3	4
Emotional/mental health related	**28**	**28**
Dementia/confusion/memory loss	5	3
Depression/paranoia etc.	5	3
Loneliness	6	8
Lack of social contact	11	13
Relationship problems	3	2
Need for emotional support	8	5
Carer related	**10**	**11**
Day care	2	3
Respite care	4	4
Other carer support	5	6
Other		
Accommodation problems	7	9
Residential care/Part III	1	0
Other/idiosyncratic	10	13

[1]Percentages represent the proportions identifying the particular problem. Clients are likely to have cited more than one.
[2]Bold type indicates summary figures for the categories indented below.

Client identified needs fall predominantly into three broad problem areas: poor health/limited mobility related; emotional/mental health related and carer related with a small residual category covering accommodation and idiosyncratic problems. More than half overall (51%) were asking for help with physical health related problems and nearly two-thirds of social work cases (64%). More than a quarter (28%) presented with emotional/mental health related problems and approximately one in ten with carer related problems.

Beyond the broad summary categories of poor health/limited mobility; emotional/mental health and carer related needs, the most frequent needs listed by clients were:

All clients/patients		**Social worker clients**	
Help with household tasks	(35%)	Help with household tasks	(41%)
More social contact	(11%)	More social contact	(13%)
Linkage (shopping, transport)	(10%)	Linkage	(13%)
Help with personal care	(8%)	Help with personal care	(11%)
Emotional support	(8%)	Accommodation problems	(9%)
		Loneliness	(8%)

The wide range of client/patient problems is evident in Table 6.1. It should be borne in mind that the problems tabulated may reflect only a sampling of the problems experienced by the respondents, i.e. only those needs which were expressed by clients or elicited by practitioners are recorded. Needs or problems not currently causing distress were not listed. The high overall proportion of elderly clients expressing needs related to emotional or mental health (28%, only 5% of which is related to confusion or memory loss), deserves comment, in the context of a service primarily perceived by elderly people as a source of household help, ADL or personal care. It is possible that many emotional needs remain unexpressed.

Also worthy of comment is the fact that during the study period, no client raised the need for help or advice related to residential care. This too is interesting in a policy context where social services are concerned with assessing for or limiting admissions to residential homes in a shift to care in the community. For the elderly clients remaining in the community is the most important goal (Wenger 1988).

As already noted above, differences between support networks were primarily reflected in the proportions of service users. In other words, those without informal help were more likely to become clients/patients. However, some relationships between presenting problems were found to be statistically significant. In terms of client identified needs, problems related to physical health and impaired mobility; need for help with household tasks and help with personal care were significantly different between networks. Table 6.2 shows the percentages and numbers of users in each network category seeking help with these problems.

Table 6.2
Client identified needs related to network type (%)(N)

Network Type	(N)	Mobility/ physical health related (p.≤003)	Help with household tasks (p.≤.03)	Help with personal care. (p.≤.05)
Family dependent	(44)	52 (23)	30 (13)	11 (5)
Locally integrated	(63)	44 (28)	21 (13)	5 (3)
Local self-contained	(39)	67 (26)	49 (19)	3 (1)
Wider community focused	(19)	84 (16)	53 (10)	0
Private restricted	(114)	42 (48)	35 (40)	12 (14)
All cases	(289)	51(148)	34 (99)	8 (23)

While more than half overall suffered from problems related to physical health or impaired mobility this was most pronounced for those with wider community focused networks, all but 3 of whom suffered from poor physical health and/or impaired mobility, as did two-thirds of those with local self-contained networks. Those with locally integrated and private restricted networks were less likely than others to present with this type of problem.

Most requests related to physical health were for help with household tasks (35%) and this too is related to network type. Again, most help is requested by those with wider community focused and local self-contained networks. While locally integrated and private restricted networks are again less likely to be asking for help with household tasks, those with family dependent networks are also less likely to ask for this help.

Although only 8% overall (23) needed help with personal care, these are most likely to be from those with family dependent and private restricted networks. However, the overall need for help with personal care is likely to be under-represented in this predominantly social work sample since much of it is likely to come from the community nursing service.

46

These findings support the second hypothesis, that clients with different types of networks make different types of demands on domiciliary services.

Practitioner identified problems and needs

The questionnaire had asked for a listing of "practitioner identified needs and problems". This was a poorly worded question, combining as it did two types of response. Data were, therefore, coded as two separate variables: practitioner identified problems and practitioner identified needs.

Table 6.3 shows the proportions of clients/patients with the listed practitioner identified problems for the whole sample and for social work clients in social work teams. Three-fifths overall and three-quarters of social work clients were identified as suffering from problems related to health or were identified as suffering from mental health related problems and more than two-fifths of all were identified as suffering from problems described here as social.

Beyond these summary categories, the most frequent practitioner identified problems were:

All clients/patients		**Social work clients**	
Disabled/limited mobility	(38%)	Disabled/limited mobility	(45%)
Family/carer stress	(24%)	Other health conditions	(24%)
Cognitive impairment/confusion	(20%)	Family /carer stress	(23%)
Other health conditions	(19%)	Sight/hearing problems	(17%)
Sight/hearing problems	(13%)	Isolation	(13%)
Isolation	(11%)	Loneliness	(13%)
Loneliness	(10%)	Rheumatism/arthritis	(11%)
Anxiety/paranoia	(10%)		

Again a wide range of problems are identified in Table 6.3. As can be seen the distinction between mental health and social problems is an arbitrary one and if these two categories are added together, one can see that even for the social work clients as large a proportion of clients suffer from mental health or social problems as suffer from problems related to health and/or mobility. A substantial minority suffer from both. Significantly larger numbers of clients are identified as suffering from problems needing other than practical solutions such as help with household tasks and activities of daily living (ADL), than clients identify themselves. This suggests that constraints may exist on asking for help with socially unacceptable problems related to mental health, relationships or personal distress unrelated to physical illness.

Table 6.3
Practitioner identified problems (%)[1]

	Study total (N=306)	Social work total (N=214)
None/None recorded	3	2
Health/mobility related[2]	**62**	**76**
Limited mobility/disabled	38	45
Rheumatism/arthritis	9	11
Heart condition	6	8
Other health condition	19	24
Sight/hearing problems	13	17
Incontinence	3	2
Falling	6	8
Pain	1	0
Post operative/hospital discharge care	-	1
Self-care related	**7**	**8**
Inadequate nutrition/not eating	5	5
Poor self-care/hygiene	4	4
Mental health related	**41**	**28**
Cognitive impairment/confusion dementia etc.	20	15
Depression/low mood	5	3
Anxiety/paranoia	10	5
Alcohol/drug abuse	2	2
Recent bereavement/grief	3	4
Wandering	3	1
Social problems	**44**	**46**
Loneliness	10	13
Isolation	11	13
Family/carer stress	24	23
Friends/neighbour stress	2	3
Physical abuse/violence	1	1
Difficult behaviour	45	2
Other	**13**	**16**
Financial/benefit related	4	5

[1]Percentages represent the proportions identifying the particular problem.
Practitioners usually cited more than one problem per case.
[2]Bold type indicates summary figures for the categories indented below.

Network type was statistically significant for two practitioner identified problems and a third at a lower level of significance as shown in Table 6.4 It can be seen from the table that family or carer stress was identified as a presenting problem in two out of five of cases involving aggregated family dependent networks (when borderline cases are excluded, 1 in 2 family dependent networks suffered from family/care stress; 1 in 3 suffered from cognitive impairment). However, a quarter of cases with private restricted networks were also found to be experiencing stress and more than half of these are networks on the family dependent/private restricted boundary of which 13 out of 17 presented with family or carer stress and 6/17 suffered cognitive impairment. Cognitive impairment was most prevalent in family dependent/ private restricted borderline networks and family dependent networks.

Also related to network type is the presence of illness other than rheumatism/arthritis or heart disease, which in many cases referred to other degenerative or terminal illnesses. These were proportionately more frequent in cases with local self-contained networks or private restricted networks. Rheumatism/ arthritis was related to network type at a lower level of statistical significance (p=.06). Despite being recorded in only 26 cases, it was proportionately higher in locally integrated and wider community focused networks, which are associated with the most independent lifestyles.

It seems important to note that 6/7 cases of incontinence were associated with private restricted networks. Cognitive impairment, including dementia, confusion and memory loss were more common in family dependent and locally integrated networks, accounting for 27/58 cases (i.e. 47% of cases in 37% of networks).

There were other indications which raise hypotheses for further research but which due to the small number of cases involved remain suggestive rather than proven. For instance, mental illness such as anxiety, paranoia, hallucinations, depression, alcohol/drug abuse appear to be associated predominantly with local self-contained and private restricted networks. Bereavement may be more problematic for those with local self-contained networks than others. Seven out of eight cases of wandering were found in private restricted networks. As reported elsewhere (Wenger and Shahtahmasebi 1990) loneliness was more common in local self-contained and wider community focused networks and isolation in local self-contained, wider community focused and private restricted networks. Six out of nine cases of financial difficulty were associated with private restricted networks. These relationships need further exploration.

Table 6.4
Practitioner identified problems related to network type (%) (N)

Network type		Family/carer stress (p=.001)	Illness other than mobility/ heart (p=.04)	Rheumatism/ arthritis (p=.06)
Family dependent	(44)	41 (18)	16 (7)	7 (3)
Locally integrated	(63)	19 (12)	14 (9)	14 (9)
Local self-contained	(39)	8 (3)	36 (14)	3 (1)
Wider community focused	(19)	16 (3)	16 (3)	16 (3)
Private restricted	(114)	26 (30)	21 (24)	6 (7)
All cases	(289)	23 (66)	20 (57)	9 (26)

Table 6.5 shows how practitioners identified client's/patient's needs. It is difficult to avoid assuming that practitioners (and clients) are likely to define need in terms of the services available. Identified needs are listed in order of prevalence of responses.

Most common is the need for help with household chores and activities of daily living, identified as needed by more than half of social work clients. All other identified needs are recognised for a fifth or fewer of clients/patients. Support for carers is mentioned most frequently, followed by companionship, social contact and emotional support. In feedback meetings social workers suggested that emotional support is grossly under-recorded since this is assumed with most cases and would not, therefore, be recorded by many of them. Supervision/monitoring appears to be a less salient need for the social work cases than overall, reflecting the importance of this need in the mental health care team.

50

Table 6.5
Practitioner identified needs (%)

	Study total (N=306)	Social work total (N=214)
None/none recorded	10	7
Household help ADL	42	55
Carer relief/support	20	18
Emotional support	17	17
Companionship/social contact	15	18
Supervision/monitoring	13	10
Help with personal care	12	16
Day care	12	12
Linkage help (shopping, transport etc.)	10	12
Housing/accommodation help	9	11
Other	9	8
Respite care holidays	8	8
Mobility aids	5	2
Modification to home	4	3
Assessment	3	2
Residential care	3	3

No practitioner-identified needs were significantly related to network type. Given the existing differences in terms of identified problems, this appears to support the contention that identified needs reflect the services available. This observation caused most comment from social work teams when the draft interim report was circulated. Subsequent discussion revealed that although they claim to be needs led, budget restrictions make it difficult not to assess on the basis of qualification for existing services. Practitioners took the view that there is no point identifying needs they cannot meet. Time to develop alternative resources or explore voluntary or group work was not perceived to be available.

There is a close relationship between client identified needs and practitioner identified needs for help with household tasks, social contact and emotional support. However, carer support and day care were less frequently identified as needs by clients. This suggests that (a) need for support of carers could be easily overlooked, and (b) that day care (perhaps like residential care) is not actively sought by clients. It is obviously important to speak to carers independently of clients.

51

Categories for client identified needs, practitioner problems and practitioner identified needs were extrapolated from responses entered on the forms. However, there is enough overlap of topics and items to allow a comparison to be made between client identified concerns and practitioner concerns. Table 6.6 looks at the proportions recording all comparable items. It can be seen that practitioners appear to recognise or identify more problems with hearing and sight; dementia/confusion; need for emotional support; and, carer related problems. The nature of these problems is such that it is easy to understand how and why clients are less likely to identify problems in these areas. It underlines the need for competent and sensitive assessments which look further than client expressed needs. It is not possible, of course, on the basis of these data to know how comprehensively such needs were recognised by social workers.

Summary - support network type and community care

It has been shown that some types of support networks make heavier demands on domiciliary support resources than others and that the type making most demands is the private restricted support network. However, different catchment areas may have different distributions of network types and this is reflected in differences in presenting problems. It has also been shown that some needs and problems are related to network type. Table 6.7 summarises problems which are more likely to occur in some networks than others.

While all problems can occur in any type of network, it can be seen that the different types of network tend to be associated with different configurations of presenting problems. The more robust network types are under-represented on case loads and most emotional and practical help comes from the informal network. As data presented elsewhere have shown, different network types represent different patterns of self-help, reciprocity and mutual aid. In some network types, when physical capacities fail the alternatives are only between struggling on alone and seeking formal help (Wenger 1993). Combined with the distribution of user's network types, this knowledge can form a useful aid to planning local services. For example, regions with high proportions of clients with family dependent and private restricted networks will have greater need for carer support services. Areas with high proportions with private restricted support networks will experience a higher level of demand than others. Budgets and services based only on demographic statistics are, therefore, unlikely to be appropriate.

Table 6.6
Client identified needs
compared with practitioner concerns
(N=36)

	Client concerns	Practitioner concerns
Says "None"	8	-
Poor health/limited mobility related	**51**	**62**
Help household tasks	35	42
Help personal care	8	12
Hearing/sight	5	13
Help bath/ADL/aids	4	5
Property modification	3	4
Linkage - shopping/transport	10	10
Emergency help/falls/alarms	3	-
Emotional/mental health related	**28**	**41**
Dementia/confusion/memory loss	5	20
Depression	5	5
Loneliness	6	10
Lack of social contact	11	15
Relationship problems	3	-
Need emotional support	8	17
Carer related	**10**	**20**
Day care	2	12
Respite care	4	8
Other carer support	5	-
Other		
Accommodation	7	9
Respite care/Part III	1	3
Other/idiosyncratic	10	13

Other differences between areas are likely as a result of local factors such as migration and employment patterns. It also seems important to note that while differences between networks are observed in terms of both client identified problems and practitioner identified problems, no difference was found in terms of practitioner identified needs. This suggests that needs were interpreted in terms of what services exist rather than in terms of presenting problems. The shift to assessments based on need, suggested in the Government's White Paper and guidance documents is yet to be evaluated. Accusations have been made in some areas that practitioners have been instructed not to record needs which cannot be met and rebuttals have followed. However, if care in the community and extended independence are to become reality, then assessments which take account of variation in **users'** needs will be imperative.

Table 6.7

Problems more likely in some networks than others; where network type is significant

	Family dependent	Locally integrated	Local self-contained	Wider community focused	Private restricted
Client identified needs	Personal care Carer support Day care Respite care		Poor health related Household tasks Accommodation	Poor health related Household tasks Carer support	Personal care Carer support Respite care Accommodation
Practitioner identified problems	Family/carer stress Cognitive impairment	Rheumatism/arthritis Cognitive impairment	Illness other than mobility/heart (Mental illness)[1] (Bereavement) (Loneliness) (Isolation)	Rheumatism/arthritis (Loneliness) (Isolation)	Family/carer stress Illness other than mobility/heart (Incontinence) (Mental illness) (Wandering) (Isolation) (Financial difficulties)

[1]Those in parentheses at lower levels of significance suggesting further exploration

55

Part IV
SUPPORT NETWORKS AND SOCIAL WORK PRACTICE

7 The consequences of variation in network type for practice

Phase 2 of the project was limited to social work teams and, unless otherwise stated, all the community care workers discussed in Part IV were members of area teams, mainly social workers, but also including two occupational therapists in one team.

Phase 2 had two related objectives: (1) for social workers to identify specific types of problems or responses which were associated with particular types of networks and which were not easily identified on the basis of earlier quantitative data; and, (2) to use the knowledge of a specific client's support network type as an indicator in planning complementary interventions. As a result of the factors discussed in Part II of this book, the first of these objectives was realised more successfully than the second. In addition to these two stated objectives, social workers commented on other aspects of the network typology which they found interesting or useful in the context of practice.

General observations about network variation

Introduction to the concept of variation in network type was generally found to be useful. Community care workers on the whole responded positively to the typology and found the different types of networks meaningful. Most were able to apply it to their experience and to immediately use it to answer pre-existing questions related to their own geographical areas. For example:

> That explains ... we found that on a large council estate ...where there is a lot of violence and social difficulty ... that the number of people receiving domiciliary services from our office was extremely small. I was quite amazed. And there is a tendency for people to say, 'Oh, well,

social services tend to spend a lot of time in G.' But in fact ... most of the elderly ladies and gentlemen who were receiving home help were living in the posh houses on the way into (town). I can see now that it's because the people on the council estate are local and integrated but it's the others who have no-one locally and have less supportive types of networks.

A related response was to see the relevance of the distribution of support network types within a caseload as potentially useful. Since the network type distribution is related to community and use of different types of domiciliary services is related to network type (Wenger & Shahtahmasebi 1990), it was recognized that knowledge of the distribution of network types within a caseload could contribute to "patch profiles" and be a useful tool in planning the local mix of services and/or types of group work.

Social workers also made some interesting generalizations about the networks and the network typology. It was recognized that in resort and retirement areas most clients had wider community focused or private restricted support networks, while those working in the mental health team in Coventry had found that most of their referrals came from those with either family dependent or private restricted networks. It was also noted that those with family dependent and locally integrated networks were less likely to suffer unrecognized needs or emergencies because they had people around them who asked for statutory help when it became necessary.

It has been shown that while most elderly people in the general population have either family dependent or locally integrated support networks, the distribution of the networks of clients of domiciliary services is quite different. The modal network type for service users is private restricted. This network type was three times more prevalent amongst clients than in the general population. It is clear, therefore, that those communities with higher proportions of private restricted networks will reflect greater demand for formal domiciliary support.

Factors and problems associated with different types of network

Chapter 6 identified those presenting problems statistically associated with different network types. In the following paragraphs, each of the network types is considered looking at further common factors identified by workers. This section discusses those factors and problems associated with different network types which were not evident from the quantitative data from Phase 1 but became apparent from the qualitative data from Phase 2. Actual cases are presented to illustrate the discussion. These case studies are based on social workers' descriptions and perceptions of the cases and are followed by the author's comments.

It became clear in the analysis of these data that it was possible to distinguish two different types of cases on the basis of the way in which the support network was functioning. The distinction is between those situations where the network appears to be functioning well but needs help to cope with the pressures of growing dependency or problems for which it is not equipped to cope; and, those networks which are not functioning well or malfunctioning and as a result are unable to handle routine or other problems.

A well-functioning network might be defined as one where its membership handles the problems of every day life routinely, recognises when help is needed and requests it. A wide range of coping capacities exists within the range of normal networks and some networks may take some time to recognize that help is needed, but in the context of social work practice or care in the community, the problems of such networks can usually be solved by service provision, advice, support or advocacy.

In contrast to well-functioning support networks are those which we can call malfunctioning. In malfunctioning networks, the support which might be expected from that support network type does not happen or happens in a maladaptive way. Malfunctioning networks may have always exhibited problem behaviours, strained or inadequate relationships or communication problems, which are exacerbated by the presence of an increasingly dependent elderly person. On the other hand, such problems may have developed **as a result** of increased dependency or the stress of coping with high levels of dependency. In either situation, these cases are more demanding of social work skills and time. They also need service inputs, advice and advocacy but often even these interventions are difficult. Help may be resisted or rejected and interventions to improve relationships, including counselling and longer-term social work support may also be indicated.

Malfunctioning networks can occur in any network type but appear to be more common amongst family dependent and private restricted ones. This reflects the fact that the proportions of elderly people in poor health are higher in these two network types (Wenger and Shahtahmasebi 1989), thus referrals and stress are also likely to occur more frequently. Networks may malfunction because of the mental or physical illness of one or more members and may be **unable** to function well. However, in some instances interventions may be able to resolve problems in relationships or communication to improve the functioning of the network. In the sections that follow cases are presented to illustrate both well-functioning and malfunctioning networks.

Family dependent support network

In the general population, elderly people with family dependent support networks were found typically to receive high standards of practical help and personal care (Wenger 1992). However, with increasing dependency it was found that help tended to become dependent on one person, most frequently an adult daughter. It was noted that loneliness and depression were common, particularly if the elderly person was housebound. These networks supported the most dependent elderly people still in the community. Requests for statutory services are likely to come late when the elderly person concerned is highly dependent.

Some problems have been identified in Chapter 6 as significantly related to network type. Most problems occurred in all network types but were more common in cases from some network types than others. Those problems which were more likely in family dependent networks were: need for personal care, carer support, day care and respite or holiday care. It was also found that family/carer stress and cognitive impairment were significantly associated with this type of network.

In comparison with population distributions, local family dependent support networks were under-represented amongst the networks of clients, suggesting that in most cases such networks support elderly people at fairly high levels of dependency without service inputs. Those with family dependent networks have been shown to be on average older and more impaired than those with different network types. Data presented elsewhere found in a longitudinal study of ageing (Wenger 1990c) that all survivors in need of short-interval care and remaining in the community, had family dependent networks. Data on contact with primary health care show that those with family dependent networks are more likely to be in receipt of care from the community nursing service (Wenger and Shahtahmasebi 1990). In most networks of this type, therefore, a high standard of care is provided. However, where heavy demands are made on the network, additional help and support may be sought from social services.

Qualitative data from discussions with social workers during Phase 2 indicate that elderly people with family dependent networks come to the attention of social workers either in the context of well-functioning networks where family members or carers are under stress and need support or relief; or, in malfunctioning networks where the level of care being provided by the informal network has given rise to concern, often in the context of pre-existing unsatisfactory relationships or the breakdown of relationships under the strain of caring. Usually more than one factor is involved. Cases ranged from straightforward requests for respite or holiday care (see Case 1 below) to complex situations involving neglect and/or abuse (see Case 2).

Based on observations from an intensive study (Wenger 1992), in the general population elderly people with family dependent networks on the whole receive satisfactory care. However, amongst the situations faced by social workers is inadequate or poor quality care. This may involve: poor management of incontinence or other aspects of personal care; elderly people being left alone for long periods of time; poor nutrition; inadequate heating; or, in a few extreme cases evidence or suspicions of physical or emotional abuse. Such cases seem to be more commonly associated with care from single sons for whom a now-elderly mother has been keeping house, although cases involving husbands and adult daughters were also cited. In rare cases, concern over possible sexual abuse may arise and this can be brought to the attention of services by concerned members of the family. Other difficulties include family relationship problems; exploitation of carers by elderly people; and, carer stress.

Case 1

Mr. A. was referred to social services by a home carer who lived in the same village. He lived with his nephew (brother's son) and the nephew's wife on an isolated farm, where he had worked all his life. He had had a leg amputated and was suffering from dementia. Because of his mobility problems he was very dependent on the family. They wanted someone to look after him while they went on two weeks holiday.

Social services arranged respite care where he enjoyed his two weeks. Although Mr. A. was spatially oriented at home, he had some trouble finding the toilet while away. Day care was offered but Mr.A. declined. His family were quite happy for him to make his own decision on this.

Comment:

Mr. A's case exemplifies the well-functioning local family dependent support network. The family needed, sought and received respite care.

It is interesting that Mr. A. was referred by a neighbour who worked as a home carer. A good example of the efficacy of local patch based care. The question could be raised as to whether respite care at home provided by a responsible sitter might be preferable for elderly people suffering from spatial disorientation. The cost-effectiveness of such a scheme might be investigated.

The offer of day care seems inappropriate, however, in the context of this type of network. Mr. A. appears to be well supported and happy and predictably turned down the offer.

Case 2

Mrs. B. lived with her son in a secluded cottage. A daughter lived in a neighbouring town but there appeared to be little contact. Her son was responsible for her care. He was identified as "not subnormal, but not quite right" and a bit of a loner.

The mother was over 80 and the son was in his early forties. He had not worked for many years. Mrs. B could not walk, was incontinent, suffering from dementia and unable to communicate. The condition of the home was described as "squalid." Cooking was apparently done over the open fire, although there was a microwave cooker in the house.

Mrs. B. had been referred to social services by concerned villagers. Concern centred on the suspicion that she was being neglected, left in a bedroom for hours at a time, was not being fed adequately and not kept warm. It was difficult to verify these allegations because Mrs. B. could not speak, but the son was known to spend long periods in the pub. A community nurse visited once a week, since the son had accepted that his mother was incontinent.

The son resisted social services involvement. Social services sought to support the son but found it difficult to communicate with him. They were attempting to establish a relationship with him but were finding it very difficult. He initially avoided contact. It was felt that he did not want people in the house but that he wanted various financial benefits, including a grant to modify the cottage. Although he realised that he could not cope with his mother on his own, he refused to discuss the situation. Conversations were filled with long silences and any discussion of his mother was resisted. Social workers felt the mother should be removed from the situation. There appeared to be no obvious easy solution.

Comment:

The case of Mrs. B. is typical of a malfunctioning family dependent support network. Such cases can be extremely time-consuming. It is likely that the son's communication problems may be long-standing, however, his reluctance to discuss his mother's situation may reflect his dependency on her and an inability to cope with her impairment and possible institutionalization. The complexity of this case makes no solution obvious but raises questions about: the responsibility of the daughter; the need for support/counselling of the son; the rights of Mrs. B. and the degree of risk that can be tolerated.

Because of the high levels of dependency often associated with family dependent support networks, sometimes accompanied by dementia, the need for sitting or holiday care in the elderly person's own home was recognized. In these cases, instead of having to leave the family home, the elderly person would remain in their familiar surroundings and a carer would care for them in their own home. Such paid carers would need to be well screened and informal family carers would need to feel secure about leaving a stranger in charge of their home but it is felt that this option would be both more appropriate and more cost-effective, particularly for dementia sufferers who become disoriented in strange environments.

Also raised by these two cases is the question of the provision of more expensive custodial services. In the case of Mr. A. the offer of day care seemed inappropriate in the context of this well functioning network. Mrs. B's situation, on the other hand, indicates that admission to residential care may be a decision which can only be postponed in the short-term. However, her case raises important questions about the inter-dependence of impaired old people and their carers. In Mrs. B's case, her son is not coping well with the situation, presumably due to low intelligence, but other situations occur where a carer's dependency on an old person leads to refusal or delay in accepting necessary help.

Locally integrated support networks

Previous work had demonstrated that in locally integrated support networks social and practical needs tend to be shared between members of the network, including family, friends and neighbours (Wenger 1992). Professional help is sought as a last resort.

Phase 1 had identified few problems which were specifically associated with this network type. However, reflecting the supportive nature of the network, which reinforces independent living, problems associated with rheumatism/arthritis and cognitive impairment were statistically associated with elderly people still living in the community in locally integrated networks. This network type was also under-represented (when compared with numbers in the population samples) in the networks of clients of social services, indicating late referrals and high levels of informal support.

Working with the social workers identified problems which earlier work had not demonstrated. Because those with locally integrated networks and their carers are well integrated into the community, the pressure that this can cause to others in the network had not previously been made explicit. Presenting problems for this group were frequently found to be associated with, on the one hand, carer breakdown or neighbour stress (Case 3); or, on the other hand with an independent personality and a determination to maintain independence (Case 4). Case 5 demonstrates both these types of problems. Cases 3 and 4 represent well-functioning networks while Case 5 shows a poorly functioning network.

Carers with locally integrated networks tend to receive support and some practical help from others in the neighbourhood. They are, therefore, often able to sustain caring without help from social services. However, if the carer becomes ill, the network tends not to have the capacity to take over completely and a crisis is presented to the statutory services.

Similarly, neighbours play an important role in this network type. Neighbours are often also friends and in the early stages of developing dependency will take on many small tasks unquestioningly. This often continues until the neighbour experiences stress. They may, for instance, receive numerous calls during the day or night from an increasingly demanding or needy elderly person involving lifting or other physical assistance with mobility. Sometimes such involvement is not recognised until a crisis occurs, a neighbour goes on holiday or an elderly person is discharged from hospital and the neighbour feels they can no longer accept the responsibility.

Case 3

Mrs. C. came to the attention of social services when her neighbour hurt his back and could no longer help her husband to care for her. Social workers were "shocked" to find that someone as disabled as Mrs. C. was still living in the community. She was completely paralysed from the neck down. Her husband - described as "a tiny frame of a man" - had taken care of her with the aid of an elderly neighbour who came to help put her to bed and to get her up. All their neighbours were very helpful. It was not until the neighbour hurt his back that they asked for help.

Comment:
Earlier intervention here may have been able to prevent injury to the neighbour either by providing help with personal care and/or lifting or by training in how to lift more safely. However, in order for this to occur, social services would need to make information available that help to those caring for highly dependent people is available.

66

Case 4

Mrs. D. had lived all her life in a northern city. At 87 she decided to move to be near her only relative, a married daughter. She moved into a ground floor flat, making a conscious decision not to move in with her daughter but to maintain her own home. She was partially sighted and suffered from impaired mobility due to rheumatism.

Soon after arrival she contacted social services and asked to attend a day care centre and for meals on wheels. She also joined a pensioners' group and a local church. Social workers identified this adaptation as related to a particular type of outgoing personality, commitment to independence and a conscious effort to become integrated into the community. Mrs. D. actively re-created the type of network she had enjoyed prior to moving.

Comment:

The fact that Mrs. D. has her own independent network, supported in part by social services, maintains her independence, morale and self-esteem. Her daughter (whom we can assume to be in her sixties) is near enough to provide reassurance and emergency care. This is a good example of preventive intervention reinforcing independence.

Case 5

Mrs. E. lived next-door to her daughter and son-in-law. She was 88, blind and subject to falls. She had a home help five days a week and attended day care once a week. She also had support from the local Crossroads group twice a week. When younger, Mrs. E. had been popular in the neighbourhood and a friend used to come and spend one evening a week with her but this had recently stopped.

Her daughter had had a nervous breakdown and suffered from other health problems as a result of which she had taken early retirement. It was when the mother had been recently registered as partially-sighted that she became known to social services. The daughter frequently telephoned the area office asking for additional help for her mother in the evenings. She was unwilling for her mother to go into residential care and said that her mother would not go, although social workers wondered about this.

There were indications that Mrs. E's network was shifting from having been locally integrated to becoming family dependent, although her daughter was apparently not prepared nor able to accept responsibility.

Comment:

Despite a locally integrated support network, albeit maybe shifting to a family dependent, social workers seem to feel that Mrs. E. would be better off in residential care. There is some indication that the daughter (whom we may assume to be in her sixties) is regarded less than sympathetically by social workers.

In the context of care in the community, the indications are that evening support for Mrs. E. and short-term counselling support for her daughter might alleviate the situation. Not being able to provide support for her mother is likely to be stressful for the daughter. Social workers may be reinforcing guilt and anxiety. Both women appear to want Mrs. E. to stay in the community in which she has friends and neighbours. Persons with this type of network are particularly receptive to the intervention of paid good neighbours and such a solution might be appropriate here. Support in the community is likely to be more cost-effective than a residential admission.

Another problem with this network type recognised by workers is the paradox of loneliness in what on first sight appears to be a situation involving many visitors to the house. However, on closer analysis this was often found to be associated with dementia or, less commonly, terminal illness. In these circumstances, visitors to the house were frequently interacting primarily with the carer and the dependent person felt lonely. This type of case was often discussed as perplexing by social workers because loneliness was not expected with this network type, particularly when there were obviously people around the elderly person. Being aware of this as a not untypical manifestation in locally integrated networks alerts workers to this likelihood, which may indicate social work counselling with the family and carer support as an alternative to day care. This approach was used in later phases of the project with considerable success.

The most typical case for those with locally integrated support networks was associated with self-referral and a commitment to the maintenance of independence. These elderly people usually suffered from impaired mobility and potential shrinking of opportunities for social contact outside the home. Help was sought to maintain independence through the services of home helps, meals on wheels and day care services.

Associated with the independent life-style of many of those with locally integrated networks is the danger of interventions which unwittingly reinforce dependency following hospitalization or other crisis. It was noted by social workers that in some instances home care organizers continued support which was intended to be temporary after the period requested by social workers without taking account of network support. Physio- and occupational therapists have also commented on the tendency of home care services to unintentionally undermine rehabilitation programmes by providing help to patients whose recovery regime includes targets for self-care or self-help. The team which had been re-organized on the basis of a neighbourhood structure had integrated the social worker and home care organiser role. This greatly reduced the size of case loads and extended social workers' local knowledge, making review easier and, it was felt, had minimized the inappropriate continuation of services. Indeed, all the complaints of reinforced dependency did come from other areas.

Local self-contained support networks

Elderly people with local self-contained support networks have been earlier identified as at risk of social isolation and likely to refuse professional help (Wenger and Shahtahmasebi 1990). They were also seen to be prone to suffer unrecognized needs and emergencies. Data from Phase 1 showed that this network type was more likely than others to be associated with problems related to poor health, restricted mobility and inadequate housing.

Very little additional information on this type of network was forthcoming from discussions with social workers perhaps reinforcing the finding that these elderly people are likely to be service refusers and to experience unrecognized emergencies.

Wider community focused support networks

Those with wider community focused support networks have been identified as being likely to make early requests for professional help but also as likely to buy in help as needed (Wenger 1992). Again, this network type was under-represented in the client sample. Data from Phase 1 indicated that old people with these networks were more likely to have problems related to poor health, especially rheumatism/arthritis, and to need carer support (Case 6). The few cases of this network type discussed with social workers supported these findings.

Earlier work has indicated that those with wider community focused networks receive more house calls from general practitioners (Wenger & Shahtahmasebi 1990) and because of their predominantly middle-class origins tend, in the face of increasing dependency, to become their own case managers buying in services as needed (Wenger 1992).

Those with wider community focused networks can usually rely on local friends for psycho-social support. However, one factor associated with this network type is the different type of relationship that seems to prevail with neighbours, compared with those with locally integrated networks. In wider community focused networks there is a reluctance to ask neighbours for help (see also Wenger and Shahtahmasebi 1991; Wenger 1992) and a less sympathetic attitude to clients from neighbours, i.e. neighbours are more likely to ask social services to intervene than to assume responsibility or provide support (Case 7). Because people with these networks live away from family, they often need only temporary help to tide them over crises, which would in many other cases be provided by local family. The same concerns about continued support reinforcing dependency apply as discussed under locally integrated support networks, although those with wider community focused networks can expect less neighbour help.

In cases where long-term help is needed, help may be bought in, although aid in finding private helpers may be needed. However, some social workers noted that the presence of privately contracted help can lead to resistance from some community care workers to the provision of statutory inputs such as home care. Assumptions that those who paid for 1-2 half-days private cleaning help could afford to pay for additional help, personal care or cooking, were cited as reasons for refusing home care interventions.

Case 6

Mrs. F. lived with her blind husband. They had one daughter who lived at the other end of the country.

Mrs. F. weighed 15 stone and was immobile having had a serious operation on one leg and was suffering from leukaemia. She went in and out of hospital frequently for blood transfusions. She was totally reliant on local authority home care but was visited frequently by local friends, one of whom came two or three times a week. She had only distant relations with the neighbours.

Comment:
A typical example of a well functioning wider community focused support network combining a high level of psycho-social support from friends with professional care.

Case 7

Miss G. lived in private sheltered housing. Social services became involved when her landlords wanted her removed from her flat. She had become very forgetful and a potential fire risk. She had had several small fires in her home. The neighbours were complaining to both the landlords and social services.

Miss G. had friends, was involved in church and communal activities and wanted to remain where she was. She felt threatened by some of the neighbours although others were supportive. Social workers were working with the neighbours and trying to convince her and those around her that what she needed was supervision. It was felt that she would not adapt well to residential care and that her physical health was good.

Comment:

A good example of constructive social work intervention. Although working with neighbours may be more difficult than in locally integrated or local self-contained networks, it is self-evident that local support and tolerance would be the solution in this case and it is likely that at least some neighbours may also be friends. Adaptation to residential care would probably be poor.

Private restricted support networks

Those with private restricted support networks have virtually no local informal help available as the name of the network suggests (Wenger, in press). In the face of growing dependency they have only professional services to which to turn. Data from Phase 1 showed that this is the most common network type of community care clients and elderly people with private restricted networks were more likely than others to present with problems associated with personal care, illness, carer support, family/carer stress, respite care and accommodation.

Those with this type of network tend to be either, on the one hand, independent personalities, self-sufficient couples or those with either a history of mental illness or personality problems i.e. persons with private restricted lifestyles; or, on the other hand, those who through bereavement or migration (or both) have lost any network that they may previously have had. The first of these two types is the more common on caseloads but the second is also common in favoured retirement destinations.

Frequently, the private restricted network reflects a life-long adaptation. Often people have always been loners, either by independent choice, as a result of personality problems (which may be related to mental illness) or because of lack of social skills or adequate socialization and adjustment.

The private restricted network occurred almost three times more frequently in the caseloads of social services teams than in general population samples. Not only were these the modal network type but cases involving private restricted networks were also likely to be most demanding of social work skills and time. Because of these factors, more cases are described in this section than in the preceding sections. Cases fell into two general categories: (1) those associated with an independent life-style who had never developed a support network who needed support as health failed and they became frail, who in the context of this network type can be seen as well- functioning networks (Case Numbers 8-12); and, (2) those who demonstrated evidence of mental illness, eccentricity or personality problems, usually with mal-functioning networks (Case Numbers 13-16).

A high proportion were single, childless and migrants to the area. Amongst those who had adopted an independent lifestyle, many were middle-class and had come to the area in which they now lived as half of a couple. Caring spouses in these situations frequently were very isolated and on bereavement often found themselves totally alone (Cases 8, 10 and 12). In some of the most distressing of these cases, the old people had only recently moved to the area hoping to solve pre-existing problems and now wished to return to the areas from which they had come. Independence and self-sufficiency had often been qualities that they had cultivated and prided themselves upon.

People who could be described as lifelong "loners" were often single women. In several cases, their history included caring for parents for lengthy periods of time (Cases 9 and 11). There was also some suggestion that elderly men and women of this age group who were homosexual may have adopted a private lifestyle as an adaptation to ostracization.

Case 8

Miss X. was a single women in her mid seventies. She had one living relative with whom she had very little contact. She suffered from arthritis and one knee was very swollen. This meant that she could no longer get to the shops, although she was able to do some shopping from a mobile shop which called. She received the minimum of home care mainly to help with shopping. She coped with housecare and personal care without help. The home carer was the only outside contact visiting the house. However, Miss X. was very self-sufficient and happy.

Comment:
In the context of the private restricted network this reflects a positive adaptation to impairment, independence maintained with minimum intervention.

Case 9

Miss S. had always been a carer. She had coped with the problems of life by getting out of the house and doing things on her own. She had had few peer relationships. When she felt down she used to go shopping or she would go out to see something interesting. She had felt very much in control of her own life. She liked to think that she did not need anyone. She wanted to do what she wanted in her own way.

When her mobility became badly impaired she came to the attention of social services. She was severely disabled and misusing her drugs. She felt she had to accept some home care support. She was angry with the social worker. It took some time to establish a relationship with Miss S. What she really wanted, the social worker was not in a position to give her - the ability to walk down the street again. She found it difficult to accept that she was losing her independence.

Comment:
The stress on independence is typical in this network type. Here the social worker was working with Miss S. to help her come to terms with her impairment.

Case 10

Mr. M. (65) and his wife had retired to the seaside. They were financially secure but had no local contacts in the area prior to retiring there. They had one daughter who lived over 50 miles away. Despite the fact that he was suffering from multiple sclerosis and osteo-arthritis, they had moved into a bungalow, which was built on two levels with steps. They had no knowledge of local services and because they had no local contacts they had no network through which they could acquire this knowledge when Mr. M. became incapacitated.

Social services were able to introduce them to a local MS group and that enabled them to find out about the services which were available locally, what they could do about adaptations and about carer support for Mrs. M. They introduced the M's to the telephone help line. Mr. M. could

73

not be left alone. Their social worker commented that if they had had a local network, they would not have needed social services help because they would probably have received all the information and support they needed through informal sources.

Comment:
Another example of difficulties which can arise from independence.

Case 11

Miss N. was 73, arthritic and living alone in a first floor flat. She had never married and the only close relationship in her life had been her mother. She had nursed her mother through three years of terminal cancer and often referred to this period. She had no relatives, no friends and only one neighbour who used to occasionally take her food. It was this neighbour who brought her to the attention of social services.

Miss N. was very much a recluse. When first approached by a social worker she resisted any help or intervention. It took three visits before the social worker was allowed entry. Miss N's hair was matted. Her toenails were so long that they had curled under and embedded themselves in the soles of her boots. She slept in her clothes. She appeared to be "mentally slow."

After much persuasion, Miss N. agreed to go to a residential home for day care. There she had a bath and her hair washed. Eventually she agreed to have her long matted hair cut off. She was referred to a specialist and her feet were attended to, but her legs were so distorted that she could only walk on her ankles.

Subsequently, after a lot of support she moved into a ground-floor warden-controlled flat. Home care helped her with the move. After months of resisting all interventions, she suddenly stopped doing anything for herself and became totally dependent. She received visits from a community nurse and home care daily but telephoned her home carer and the warden frequently. Eventually, she hardly moved from her chair until one night she fell off it and was taken to hospital. In hospital she took to a wheelchair and it was thought to be unlikely that she would resume the struggle to live alone.

Comment:

The association between long-term caring and private restricted networks was a frequent one. The transitional period of day care is likely to make the acceptance of residential care easier (see discussion below).

Case 12

Mrs. J. was 77 and lived alone on an isolated farm to which she and her husband had retired. They had no children. Two nephews living in different parts of the country kept in touch from time to time. Her husband had recently died which resulted in her being referred to social services. Mrs. J. had not realized how ill she herself was because she had been so pre-occupied looking after her husband. She was nearly blind, suffered from cirrhosis of the liver and multiple other medical conditions.

When the J's retired they had joined many local groups where they had managed to alienate most of the local people by trying to reorganize their lives for them. They were not accepted from the start. They had been breeding cats and dogs and she had had goats, ducks and chickens. She still had two dogs and five cats. During the time her husband was ill she had had a young lad from the village to help her but due to her blindness he had been able to steal most of her valuable possessions such as small antiques.

Mrs. J. could not stand on her feet for very long and could not cook or feed the animals. She was receiving home help five days a week and frozen meals. She had a small additional pension which was only £1 over income support but which made her ineligible for additional allowances. She was determined to remain in her own home with her dogs and cats and steadfastly resisted moving into residential care. She had no contact with the community.

Comment:

Another example of the potential impact of caring - the neglect of the carer's health. This is something that GP's, community nurses and social workers should keep an eye on. Carers need separate assessments. Some intervention or support during her husband's illness may have protected both her health and her property. But again elderly people need to know that help is available although they may resist any intervention.

Note that Mrs. J. is "resisting" residential care. This suggests that social workers see this as an appropriate solution. However, it is possible that Mrs. J. would not respond well to communal life because she has always been independent. There are indications of earlier overtures to local groups and it may be that Mrs. J. would accept a paid good neighbour, which could ultimately re-establish local links.

A high proportion of cases discussed by social workers had elements of mental illness associated with the presenting problems (Cases 13 and 16). Some had a history of mental problems and previous hospitalization. Others had a history of conflict in relationships and alienation of others including those who sought to help them including both informal and statutory carers (Cases 14 and 15). These behaviours were often associated with self-neglect.

One of the most interesting findings of this phase of the study was the way in which many of those with private restricted networks adapted to residential care (Case 16). While bereaved spouses of independent couples often adapted well to small (usually private) homes, many in this private restricted category adapted very poorly to residential care. This was particularly marked where they had lived what may be termed a private restricted life, i.e. they had always been isolates. Lack of adaptation to residential care manifested in a range of behaviours. Some exhibited psychiatric symptoms which were not displayed prior to admission. For instance, shouting in the night or aggressively demanding attention. Several of the more extreme cases were identified by the clinical psychologist on the Coventry mental health team. She had been subsequently called in to deal with management problems in the residential homes. In most cases, symptoms which had not been displayed before admission were identified as being triggered (but not necessarily caused) by the residential home environment. It was seen as inappropriate to expect life-long loners, adjusted to a solitary lifestyle, to adapt easily or well to a communal living situation. Similar responses to residential care were observed in the other teams. Observed behavioural responses included: withdrawal; refusal to eat; temper tantrums; shouting; a suicide attempt; and repeated demands to return home (occasionally successful).

Case 13

Miss T. was a 75 year-old spinster showing the first signs of dementia. She was brought to the attention of social services by friends who lived in another part of the country. When they paid her an annual visit they had noticed that she was failing both physically and mentally.

It took the social worker a long time to gain Miss T's confidence. She lived in a private second-floor flat and had adopted a very privatised lifestyle. At first, she did not want anyone in her flat. She had one sister who lived abroad from whom bundles of presumably unanswered letters were found. At times she would lock herself in her bedroom and refuse to come out or answer the door. On more than one occasion the police broke into the flat because she refused to answer and raised concern about her safety. She used to hoard and hide things, including food.

Miss T. had a local reputation of being very eccentric but friendly, although very private. She always wore trousers and had her hair cut like a man. Social services offered home care and day care. She accepted home care and became very attached to her social worker whom she always greeted with a hug. She could not accept day care because she found it too large a place with too many people around. Subsequently, she accepted a place in a very small private residential home where she settled down well. At first, she remained in her room and took all her meals there but later she mixed freely with other residents and seemed content.

Comment:
A successfully handled case which resulted in a favourable outcome. Miss T. was gradually eased out of a withdrawn situation into a compatible residential setting.

Case 14

Ms. W. (marital status unknown), 92, was a long-standing case. She was described as having "fallen out with absolutely everybody she knows." She appeared to thrive on conflict with her neighbours and had always been the same. It was felt that it was not only her problem but that there had been provocation from the neighbours. They had been throwing things at her dog and had threatened her with a gun, to which she retaliated with a big stick!

Ms. W. received home care support with whom she regularly fell out. Eventually, she decided that she could not manage on her own any longer and her GP arranged for her admission to a private nursing home. When she arrived she had soiled her clothing. They decided to give her a bath. She did not want a bath and struggled with four care attendants who manhandled her into the bath. For six days she refused to eat, she had tantrums and tried to commit suicide by breaking a glass and trying to cut her wrists - in full view of care staff.

A friend had offered to take her to stay for a fortnight (after which the friend was returning abroad). Ms. W. wanted to return to the community but her social worker felt it unlikely that she would be able to go home.

Comment:

The problems of quality of care in private establishments is likely to become a more pressing one and raises important questions for the inspectorate.

It is unclear why Mrs. W. would not be able to go home but such situations often result from precipitate loss of tenancies. It is hoped that admissions to residential institutions will become more flexible if more care in the community becomes available.

Case 15

Mrs. P. had lived in the same town most of her life. Her daughter lived nearby but Mrs. P's behaviour made it very difficult for her daughter to get on with her, although she had said she was willing for her mother to live with her. However, the daughter's husband and son threatened to leave if Mrs. P. came to live with them.

Mrs. P. was very physically incapacitated and dependent on help. She was convinced, however, that everybody who came to help had some self-seeking motive. She was so abusive that the area team had to rotate home carers on a regular basis.

Mrs. P. was very manipulative of her daughter and her daughter found herself in between her mother and her husband and son. Her daughter, who was also described as having a difficult personality, often walked out and said she was never going back. She felt guilty about not giving more support but visited less and less frequently. Mrs. P. had one old friend who had recently given up coming to visit her because Mrs. P. had said the only reason she came was to keep warm and save on her own gas and electricity!

Mrs. P. was described as highly intelligent and articulate. She had apparently always had the same personality. She had been referred to a clinical psychologist and seemed to be pleased with this attention. She was extremely lonely, had always been so and, as her social worker said, "You can understand why."

Comment:

The management of mental illness in the community is underdeveloped. In this case, social work support for the family might make it possible to work in partnership and could possibly shift the network towards a family dependent one, but only if consistent formal support to the family continued.

Case 16

Miss L. came to England from Ireland after the war. She had lived alone for many years after the death of her mother and was a very solitary person. Following the breaking of her leg, she was admitted to a Part III home because it was felt that her mobility was too impaired for her to live alone. She had also been suffering from acute confusional states, although this was subsequently thought to be the result of a urinary infection.

She was referred to a clinical psychologist because she became a management problem for the residential home. She was screaming for hours each night and demanding attention. The other residents got up a petition asking for her removal.

Subsequent work by the GP, CPN and psychologist helped Miss L. to work through her problems which stemmed from the nature of the regime of the home and her loss of control and independence. It brought back all the frustrations of living with a very controlling mother. After living very privately in the community the group environment was also difficult to adjust to. Sadly, it seemed that Miss L. would have been able to return to the community where she could have managed with some domiciliary support but her home had been disposed of.

Comment:

This case represents a typical reaction to residential care from life long isolates. It is clear that communal living is often an inappropriate solution. Here again, the precipitate loss of the existing home precluded return to the community. Better understanding of these factors could lead to more cost-effective use of residential beds.

Borderline cases

As discussed in Chapter 5, because networks are ideal types, not all situations fit neatly into one type or another. Using the PANT instrument in Phase 1, 3% of cases were inconclusive and 23% were borderline cases. Previous work had shown that shifts in network type occur (Wenger 1990b). Shifts are in most cases from stronger network types to more vulnerable network types and tend to be associated with deterioration in physical or mental health. It is, therefore, possible to see some borderline types as evidence of shifts in network type.

Shifts from locally integrated to family dependent networks are one of the commonly expected shifts and 8% of cases were on this borderline. This shift reflects the capacity of many locally integrated support networks to become family dependent in the face of growing dependency as family members take on responsibility for care and friends and neighbours withdraw, especially in the context of dementia or other mental problems or terminal illness.

Another expected shift is from wider community focused to private restricted network type and 4% of cases were on this borderline. This shift can also be expected in the context of growing dependency where friends may dissociate themselves in the face of failing capacities. Although they may continue to provide emotional support to carers, they may withdraw from the dependent elderly person in the context of less socially acceptable behaviour or problems, such as dementia, incontinence or loss of speech following stroke. In the absence of local family the network becomes private restricted.

Other generalizations can be made about the wider community focused/private restricted network. Old people on this network borderline (Case 17) appear to be frequently those whose deteriorating health brings with it a recognition of vulnerability and withdrawal from reciprocal relationships (Wenger, 1993), which may have been fairly superficial or activity related. In the face of health problems, high anxiety levels may occur coupled with growing dependency on statutory workers.

Another borderline, not identified in the study based on a general population sample, accounted for 8% of borderline cases in Phase 1. This was the borderline between family dependent and private restricted networks. The significant presence of this borderline amongst "cases" suggests that this represents a sub-type of network, i.e. where an elderly person has become housebound and a family carer cares in relative isolation. A high proportion of networks identified on this borderline were in need of carer relief or support and respite or holiday care.

Cases on the family dependent/private restricted borderline appear to include those where carers are trying to provide adequate care under difficult and often isolated circumstances. Care in these cases may not be adequate and elderly persons may relinquish goals rather than make demands on relatives whom they perceive to be under strain. In other cases, the standard of care causes concern due to neglect or inadequacy of commitment to care. Cases 18 and 19 described in this section illustrate these situations, but Case 2 described in the section on Family Dependent Networks obviously approaches this borderline.

Case 17 (Wider community focused/private restricted)

Mr. Q: lived alone. He was diabetic and frequently not managing his insulin adequately. He had been admitted to hospital on more than one occasion. When facing discharge he was extremely anxious and all the professionals around him were 'in a panic.' A visit from the home care organiser was arranged but when he got home and she called he would not accept any help. He wanted to be independent. This was a recurrent pattern.

After being at home for some time, where he was socially isolated, his condition deteriorated and he was re-admitted to hospital. He recognised that he needed more help and a package of care was arranged for him but his social worker was not at all sure that he would accept it once he arrived home. He was worried that he would not be able to cope alone and talking about going into residential care. However, his social worker felt that once home he would forget about residential care. His main problem seemed to be anxiety engendered by social isolation and failing health. Sadly, what he appeared to need was emotional support and contact but this was not available.

Comment:

If more highly dependent old people are to be maintained in the community, cases like this will become even more common. In this case, the hospital social worker felt that she wanted to provide regular emotional support in the community but the resources were not available, as a result Mr. Q. seemed to be on a regular carousel in and out of hospital. This pattern would appear to be a very expensive option for statutory services, when it would appear that emotional support in the community could play an important preventive function.

Case 18 (Family dependent/private restricted)

Mrs. V. (88) was a client of a hospital social worker. She had been in hospital for surgery. She was very reluctant to discuss her home situation with the social worker but gradually it became clear. She lived with her husband who was older than she and was obviously struggling to cope. Her husband had a brother living nearby who was very helpful but was caring for an invalid wife himself. Mr. and Mrs. V. had no children but they received some help and support from nephews. Their neighbours were friendly and called in to see them once a week.

Mrs. V. was unable to go out. She reluctantly accepted the offer to discuss their situation with the home care organizer and subsequently agreed to have home care once a week. She herself had little contact with informal helpers but her husband did receive some support.

Comment:

While not knowing all the facts of this case, reluctance to discuss or admit to difficult situations is not uncommon amongst elderly people. Often the cause is a fear of compulsory institutionalisation. This is likely to be most pronounced amongst those who have prided themselves on their independence - such as many of those with wider community focused or private restricted networks.

Case 19 (Family dependent/private restricted)

Mrs. Y. was 77 and lived with her daughter, son-in-law and grown grandchildren. She lived in the same house but had little contact with the family. Her meals were brought to her room. Her son-in-law brought her a cup of coffee in the morning and her grandson came in to turn on her television in the evening. She had been mainly in bed for over four years, although she was able to get out of bed. She was known to go to the kitchen when alone in the house and it was felt she could do more than she admitted.

She came to the attention of social services when her daughter asked for respite care. Mrs. Y. was visited by a bath attendant once a week and it was the community nursing service who contacted social services. Mrs. Y. wanted to go to day care and to have more contact with other people. She felt isolated. However, attendance at an Age Concern day centre was unacceptable and she only went once because the people there were too old!

This was a puzzling case. The mother claimed that the family had taken over. The family were reluctant to discuss the situation. The possibility of a history of child abuse in the past was mentioned. It was difficult to know whether the mother had withdrawn from the family or if the family had deliberately excluded her. A WC had been installed unscreened in the corner of her dingy room since the case was opened. It was clear that she had a very poor diet served to her in her room erratically at inappropriate times and apparently consisting of sandwiches. The daughter explained that Mrs. Y's mother had also retired to her bed in her 70's and that Mrs. Y. was copying her.

82

Despite the presence of a large family in the house Mrs. Y. was effectively isolated.

Comment:

A complex case of a malfunctioning network, which indicates a need for longer-term discussion and counselling. Again, a case where the potential of a family dependent network exists but where solutions are unlikely to be immediate.

Summary and discussion

Phase 2 confirmed statistical findings from Phase 1 which showed that there are relationships between some presenting problems and network type. The qualitative data from the second phase demonstrated problems associated with network type which had not necessarily been apparent in Phase 1. These are summarised in Table 7.1 and it is suggested that these factors should be taken into account in practice. It may be useful to compare this table with Table 6.7.

Phase 2 also identified differences within network types, which may be summarised in terms of the needs of well-functioning networks and malfunctioning networks for each type. Although well-functioning networks are less likely to make demands on statutory services, both well-functioning and malfunctioning networks are likely to require service inputs, particularly in the face of growing impairment and for each network type typical situations for both well-functioning and malfunctioning networks occur. For example, in well-functioning family dependent support networks, carers may provide a high standard of care but may be under considerable stress; in malfunctioning networks carers may be inadequate for the task or be unable to ask for help leading to neglect and in some cases abuse. These types of differences are illustrated in the case studies presented in this book.

This section on the factors and problems associated with different types of network has shown that support networks tend to be associated with different configurations of problems. The qualitative data reinforce the quantitative findings and provide additional support of the hypothesis that different support networks are associated with different demands on statutory services. It has been shown that both well functioning and malfunctioning networks need social work support and drawn attention to the fact that work with malfunctioning networks is much more demanding of skill, time and resources.

In the presentation of cases in this section some attention has been paid to the types of interventions provided. In most cases, these have been appropriate and supportive but two points deserve comment. In the first place, a clear emphasis on service provision emerges rather than interventions based on a counselling or a psycho-therapeutic approach. Despite a stated preference for one-to-one counselling, the latter approach appears paradoxically to be seen as too time-consuming in a context of resource shortage rather than ameliorative or preventive. In the second place, day care and residential care sometimes appear to be seen as preferred solutions even when, in some cases, clients or their families do not request and subsequently reject such care. Both of these responses, appear to be related to resource scarcity in terms of (a) social worker time and (b) community support services. Both appear to result in less cost-effective interventions being planned.

Table 7.1
Factors associated with network types identified in Phase 2

Family dependent	Locally integrated	Local self-contained	Wider community focused	Private restricted
Precipitating factors related to carer stress (particularly if carer becomes isolated)	Precipitating factors carer breakdown/illness	(Inadequate data)	Involvement of neighbours resisted	May adapt poorly to residential care
Inadequate care may occur	Neighbour support common but neighbour stress may occur		Need for short term help common	Mental illness and difficult personalities common
Residential care solutions may be resisted	Loneliness resulting from lack of emotional contact rather than isolation		Contracting of private help common	Carers often caring in isolation
Professional respite care in the home may be needed where dementia occurs.	Maintenance of personal autonomy very important to elderly persons who live alone			

8 Using network type in practice

The second objective of Phase 2 was for social workers to use the identification of network type as a practice tool. It had been envisaged that given knowledge of the network typology, knowing the support network type of a given client would make it possible to use that knowledge to design interventions which were compatible with the type of support network which existed in each case. The cases presented in the previous section come from this phase of the work.

Suggestions regarding some of the implications of network type for practice had been presented in the draft **Guide for Practitioners** (Wenger 1990a). These related to: the situation of carers; work with or through neighbours; bereavement support; and, home nursing. It was anticipated, however, that social workers would take account of the different networks in the typology and devise different strategies accordingly. As noted above, this part of the project was less successful than had been hoped, although some progress was made.

Part of the responsibility for the less than total success of this aspect of the work rests on the adequacy of the training provided by the researcher to participating teams. After reading the draft of this part of the book, all teams endorsed the need for more detailed training in the application of network type. Indeed, the development and refinement of training materials was one of the objectives of the PANT project. The lessons learned from this part of the work are discussed in greater detail below but first it is necessary to describe the response of the teams to the use of network type in their day-to-day working.

It became clear to the researcher only towards the end of the project that, for most of the teams, writing down elicited information or taking notes was felt to interfere with the therapeutic nature of the social work interview. Similar responses have been recorded by Caldock (1991) in her work with other social work teams. This was also confirmed by responses to a draft report, for example:

... it is somewhat foreign to traditional social work practice to make notes whilst interviewing clients and some of the social workers, therefore, found the forms difficult to use" (hospital social work team leader).

The primary aim of interviews, particularly initial interviews, was seen to be the establishment or development of a relationship with the client.

In the initial interview, when you go to assess, you also want to start a relationship going with the client. I don't know if we can do that, just asking these questions very quickly. You want to build a relationship on the conversation you are having. But I suppose you could ask these questions in the conversation." (Reference to the network assessment instrument.)

Writing was generally kept to a minimum and for some a presumption against writing anything down existed. Case notes were written up later in contexts ranging from immediately in the car following the interview to 3-4 days after the meeting. Where this was discussed, the reasons given for not taking notes in interviews were said to be based on sound practice. This reasoning seems misplaced since the relationship with clients is a professional one in which note-taking is culturally defined as appropriate, even expected, behaviour. Qualitative data from this study and that conducted by Caldock (1991) suggest that the notes written following the interview are often incomplete or inaccurate. This can lead to difficulties if other workers subsequently need to rely on notes, which is likely to become more common as the policy guidance recommendations are implemented. In the context of a shift to more intensive, multidisciplinary assessments the practice raises deep concern.

In training sessions before Phases 1 and 2, workers were asked to complete the network assessment instrument with the client, filling in the responses question by question. In Phase 1, most participating social workers handled this request by explaining to clients that they were helping with some research. They reported that the elderly people involved were interested and pleased to be helping. However, some social workers in Phase 1 and more in Phase 2 felt that it was inappropriate to use the form in the presence of the client. In some instances this resulted from the crisis nature or the sensitivity of the interview, in others from the social worker's perception of correct practice. In these cases, answers to the 8 questions were gleaned either because the subject came up naturally or by working them into the discussion. Some found it difficult to imagine using the form in a client interview:

> In a way you always do assess their lifestyle and so on. It is just that you have to do that (PANT form) before you can start any work. I don't know if we could just go in there and ask these questions and circle... I don't think we can do it mechanically. You still have to do the interviewing by going round it....

On the other hand, there were also indications that questions in the PANT instrument were **not** routinely asked:

> Have I learnt anything that I wouldn't normally ask? The only clue possibly is, 'How often do you see any of your children or other relatives?' That might give me a lead - you know, warning bells. What's going on here? But then he would tell me that anyway ....

It had been hypothesized that the network typology might have greatest usefulness in initial interviews with potential new cases, when social workers needed to discover most information about a new client. Knowing the support network type, it was suggested, provided a short-cut to establishing the social context. But questions arose concerning the accuracy of responses based on social workers' interpretations:

> Sometimes I felt that if I'd filled a form on behalf of a client I might have got them private restricted. And when I filled it in with the client it's come out as family dependent.

In addition, the interview and assessment methods which were used sometimes precluded the discovery of network type during the first interview if the topics covered in the instrument seemed inappropriate. This made it impossible in these cases for social workers to incorporate knowledge of network type into the immediate planning of interventions. One team leader identified the magnitude of the change envisaged:

> I think that for most workers, assessment systems are still resource led and that it requires **a major paradigm shift** to take on board the idea of network type and the extent to which this might affect the level and type of demands an individual may make on a service. (emphasis added)

She felt that most practitioners saw assessment as related to levels of dependency or emotional problems and noted that assessment of need generally viewed support or interventions quantitatively rather than qualitatively in terms of the type of support or help that would be appropriate. Similar observations have been made by the author in discussions of assessment with practice managers. It seems that the change in practice that the project sought to bring about was of a greater degree than had been realised. The team leader quoted above suggested that the use of the network typology should be targeted on planners and policy development officers.

Feedback meetings after Phase 2 indicated that some social workers had misunderstood the proposed use of network type. As reported above, a few interpreted the aim as being to change the existing network - changing a family dependent network into a locally integrated network, for instance. Some concern was expressed about ethical considerations because they felt that taking account of informal support discriminated against caring families or communities. This constrained their efforts to make use of the typology.

One other factor interfered with the integration of network type into practice. All teams had negotiated a minimum number of forms to be completed in Phase 1. It had originally been hoped that in Phase 2 the form would be used with all new cases at initial interview and in all reviews. However, social workers preferred to again negotiate a minimum number of forms. This had the effect of limiting the number of cases in which knowledge of network type became an available practice tool. It also had the effect of making assessment of network type an optional extra completed as a favour to the researcher, rather than as an added tool in the social worker's repertoire, while at the same time limiting the wider understanding of the typology which use with a large number of cases would have provided.

Despite these constraints, some progress towards the use of knowledge of network type in practice was made. Many social workers commented on the fact that the network typology made their work more interesting or easier:

> You develop that kind of way of thinking. It is only in that sense that I think that it would be useful in that you are going in there with preconceived ideas of ... and network types as well. As you say, one can more or less predict the levels of dependency and the kind of services that would be appropriate for this particular family (on the basis of network type), so in that sense I think it is very useful.

Just recognising the network type of clients explained many of the differences between them. Comments such as, "...then when I found out that he was wider community focused, I knew why......" were not infrequent. It was less easy for social workers to use the knowledge of network type in planning interventions:

I think that it is a very useful thing because it formalises things without putting labels on people. It is a diagnostic tool in a way. I have difficulties about packages of care though - how one would design certain services to meet certain network types.

While social workers had difficulty with using network type in designing specific interventions, they quickly picked up on associations with network types which had significance for particular categories of networks:

1   Early findings, related to the possible negative response by some clients with private restricted support networks to residential care, were fed back to subsequent teams. Social workers found that this information not only explained experiences they had had in the past, but alerted them to the need to consider the possible responses of clients who fitted the criteria which appeared to be associated with this reaction. Greater caution and attention to network type appeared to develop in assessments for residential care. Domiciliary alternatives and placements in small (usually private) residential homes came to be seen as more appropriate for life-long loners or very independent old people with private restricted networks.

2   Awareness of potential neighbour stress in locally integrated support networks became something which social workers began to look out for and take account of on a more regular basis.

3   Social workers working in retirement areas where a high proportion of support networks were wider community focused or private restricted became aware of the fact that carers in these types of networks were likely to care in relative isolation (without local supportive family) and to receive little practical and/or emotional support explaining the high need for carer support and respite care which existed in their workloads.

In other instances, knowledge of network type sometimes made it difficult to understand why a particular problem existed. Loneliness is not infrequent amongst the presenting problems faced by social workers. Usually it is associated with social isolation and by many may be equated with isolation. The basic practice response appears to be the offer of day care. Loneliness in family dependent and locally integrated support networks seemed to be contradictory to some social workers. Day care was often rejected by these clients. In most cases, closer analysis of a case would indicate that the problem related to the marginalization of the client within the home. Data from earlier work (Wenger 1990c) show that very dependent old people may withdraw from confiding in their carer because they feel that they are enough of a burden without sharing their sadness or worries. Often there were many people coming and going but the client still felt lonely:

> This lady was saying her main problem was loneliness; she was lonely and she was isolated. She was misusing drugs ... People to protect themselves, were keeping their distance. ... She definitely had a lack in her life of social interaction. People would come in and more or less say 'Hello, how are you?' But they didn't want to stay and talk to her because they couldn't handle it (very manipulative personality). Especially the family couldn't handle it. Her son didn't want to know.

These situations were often associated with dementia or terminal illness. In discussion, social workers recognized that these cases were often different from loneliness in, say, private restricted support networks, and therefore demanded different responses. Interventions based on social work with the client and their carer/family were perhaps more appropriate than day care. However, as noted above, the impression was gained that long-term counselling interventions to resolve problems in relationships or lack of communication were not often seen as possible because of constraints of social worker time. The same was true of preventative interventions generally.

The last paragraph generated considerable response from social workers when these findings were circulated in a draft report. These types of intervention were indicated as preferable to social workers but excluded by the managerial expectations of service prescriptions. A senior social worker felt that prevention and counselling were a real need but that social work was increasingly dominated by service provision. It is suggested that some service interventions, such as admissions to residential care, may be more time-consuming and resource costly than focused preventative or counselling help. Assessment of network type could help to identify situations where planned counselling interventions were likely to be more effective than service provision.

While this phase of the project was somewhat disappointing in terms of the use social workers were able to make of the network typology in planning interventions/packages of care, it is felt in retrospect that this reflects shortcomings in the training provided by the project. It became clear that it was only towards the end of the project, when specific cases were discussed, that the social workers began to understand the potential of the typology. As noted, one team asked the researcher to return to work with them further on the implications for packages of care. After reading the draft report, one team leader commented that "the instrument has made us aware of the need to refine intervention in a way that is compatible with the type of support network ....". In fairness, some of the generalizations which can be made on the basis of network type, are similar to information that good social workers were able to elicit from interviews. However, often this information appeared to be partial, and when workers' identified network type as different from that shown using the instrument, subsequent questioning and discussion usually indicated that the instrument assessment was more accurate.

All workers participating in the project had been given a draft of **Support Networks of Elderly People: A Guide for Practitioners** (Wenger 1990). It had been expected that this guide would be written on the basis of information from Phases 1 and 2 of this project but it became clear early in the study that more information was needed on which social workers could base their participation in the project. A full Guide could not have been produced without the study, but paradoxically the success of the study demanded a guide for practitioners! A final version of the Guide is now available (Wenger 1994).

It is clear that social workers would benefit from more guidance of the ways in which identification of network type can be used in practice and this will be incorporated into the revised Guide. In preparing training sessions and materials greater attention is now placed on: (1) familiarization with the various network types; and (2) applications of network type to practice. It is anticipated that the identification of network type will be used as an indicator of which questions then need to be asked to determine appropriate interventions.

Despite the training shortcomings identified in the research project design, it was evident that many of the participating social workers found the network typology a useful tool and it is felt that with the greater familiarity that comes from frequent use, its use can be usefully integrated into community care practice. It is, therefore, felt that the fourth hypothesis presented at the end of Chapter 1, that **knowledge and understanding of variation in support network type is likely to be a useful tool for community care practitioners at the level of the individual and the team**, has been supported at the level of the individual worker. However, no attempt was made to build up consistent team profiles of network type so that the usefulness for teams as a whole has still not been adequately tested. The findings have shown, however, that identification of a user's support network type can be used constructively by community care workers to inform interventions which are complementary and compatible with that particular type of network.

9   Summary and conclusions: Network assessment and practice

What the PANT Project has demonstrated is that variation in support network type has important implications for policy and practice in community care. It has shown that while many common problems occur in most types of networks, the distribution of problems between networks differs and some difficulties are more likely to be associated with specific types of networks. More particularly, the high proportion of private restricted support networks on caseloads, despite their small proportion in general populations, underscores the vulnerability of elderly people with this type of network.

The more robust network types, namely the family dependent and locally integrated support networks, are associated with stable residence patterns (Wenger and Shahtahmasebi 1989), resulting in the presence of local kinship networks. The more vulnerable support networks, particularly the private restricted support network, are associated with geographical relocation in middle age or on retirement. The distribution of support networks has been shown to be related to community or neighbourhood (p=.01), so it can be seen that local patterns of migration are likely to affect network distribution and thus the level of demands on local agencies.

Different problems and difficulties are associated with different network types and work with the pilot teams has shown that community care workers can use network type as a diagnostic tool which can be used as an indicator in planing interventions. However, it became obvious that practitioners need a thorough understanding of the network typology before the identification of support network type can become meaningful or useful. In part this was accomplished with teams which entered the pilot phase late by the production of sample chapters of a planned handbook. As practitioners became more familiar with the typology its usefulness became more apparent to them. For example, initial resistance to "labelling", reflected in early reservations, was overcome as social workers acquired a clearer idea of the applications and usefulness of the typology. This raises important questions about the need for adequate training in the understanding of the network typology **prior** to the use of the instrument.

It also became clear as a result of pilot work, that the instrument is likely to be best suited as a screening assessment tool which will serve to indicate both other lines of questioning and types of appropriate service interventions. Where a practitioner already has an intimate knowledge of a user as a result of long association, the instrument is probably less useful. However, social workers' impressions were sometimes proved wrong when explored in the context of conflict with the instrument. Given the wide range of correlations with demographic variables (Wenger and Shahtahmasebi 1989) and service use (Wenger and Shahtahmasebi 1990), the PANT instrument can be recommended as a short assessment form. In some cases, it can be appropriately used as an alternative to longer assessment forms and in others as a short-cut to cue workers as to profitable areas for exploration.

The indications are that knowledge of network type is primarily useful to those with a responsibility for decisions to introduce interventions, e.g. social workers, who put together a service/intervention package. It is unlikely to be of use to home care organizers or community service officers when they are implementing the decisions of others. However, a blurring of roles is likely in the reorganization which followed the implementation of the community care legislation and understanding network type variation is likely to become useful for a wide range of service providers. It may be of less use to community nurses who provide specific treatments but may become so if they assume a case or care manager role. With increasing emphasis on assessments, the instrument has the potential to be a useful component in the context of case/care management as a screening instrument. For example, subsequent to the study, the Coventry team reported that community services and social workers now screen all those 75+ and refer on to the mental health care team as appropriate. It was suggested that the PANT instrument would be of use at this more primary level of assessment.

The PANT instrument is likely to be most useful when used with new cases, as part of a screening assessment, by community care workers with responsibility for putting together service packages. In this context, it is likely to serve as a predictive tool in both planning appropriate interventions and estimating the long-term needs of the user. However, re-assessment of network type should form part of routine reassessments since shifts in network type are likely amongst clients/patients with advancing age and such shifts will indicate adjustments in support interventions.

Efforts to introduce assessment of network type into practice and use of this knowledge met with some success. However, in addition to providing information on the relevance of network type to practice, the exercise also highlighted some of the problems associated with the introduction of innovation into established working patterns. Because of the broad implications of the network typology, it has been suggested that planners and policy-makers may also be a relevant target for training!

It became clear in the course of the study that, in addition to some basic resistance to change which needs to be overcome with any innovation, innovation is unlikely to be accepted readily in a context of organizational change which engenders uncertainty and anxiety. On the other hand, where change is handled collaboratively in a supportive environment and/or where innovation is perceived to make it possible to achieve shared goals and provide a higher quality of service or care, it is likely to be accepted and incorporated into working practice.

In terms of the network typology, on the basis of the experience gained, it is clear that network type is relevant for practice but that community care workers will need explicit guidance in terms of the relationships between network type and different forms of intervention. It is clear that the introduction of use of network assessments into social work practice will require adequate training in the nature of the different network types and their characteristics. The relevance of variation in support network types for social work practice suggests that attention to such variation should become part of basic social work training. Training for community care workers will need to include practice in service packaging and the design of interventions based on different types of networks. **Support Networks of Elderly People: A Guide for Practitioners** (Wenger 1994) will be matched with a training package, including suggested handouts and exercises now available in collaboration with BASE.

In general, community care workers found the network typology meaningful in that they recognized the distinctions between the different types and found them useful in making generalizations about clients. They had more difficulty in using knowledge of network type in practice but **were** able to incorporate associations between specific problems, network types and appropriate interventions once these had been made explicit. One team leader recognized that "we are not always as aware as we might be of the coping capacities that exist in normal networks".

The potential of using the assessment of network type on a case by case basis to establish aggregate 'patch', neighbourhood or team profiles was also recognised by some workers. Although it was also accepted that few data of this type existed, patch profiles based on network type were seen as potentially useful in "identifying and planning the local mix of services for consumers". One of the participating teams has indicated that they may now adopt this approach.

The need for social workers to work closely with informal networks has been described as fundamental to the practice of community social work (Hadley et al. 1987). This perspective is likely to become increasingly appropriate in the shift to the provision of care in the community. It has been suggested that social network assessment will become increasingly important after 1993. Seed (1990) comments that social network analysis can form a framework for social work assessments and reviews, including needs-led assessments:

> It is clear that an understanding of social networks, especially of home-based networks around informal care, will be central to the successful new approach to social care and case management which is envisaged. (p.7)

However, he makes his suggestions in the context of the potential introduction into social work practice of complex analyses using diagrams and lengthy forms. It is felt that the PANT instrument based on 8 essential questions offers a simpler, more user-friendly route to similar assessments.

Criticisms directed at a social network approach to social policy provision (e.g. Collins 1991; Trevillion 1992) rightly take issue with government documents which present an undifferentiated image of support networks and appear sometimes to assume that all elderly people have (or should have) long-established locally integrated networks. What the network typology does is to urge a more critical network approach by identifying the realities of weak and ineffective support networks as well as robust ones.

In the context of the implementation of the recommendations of the White Paper therefore, use of the PANT instrument as an assessment tool would seem to have particular applicability. As a screening instrument, on the basis of 8 questions it is possible to identify support network type which has been shown to have a significant relationship with a range of presenting problems. It also has considerable predictive validity, e.g. the coping capacity of carers and their needs for emotional support and instrumental help. (N.B. Carers' networks may be different from the networks of their dependent relative and must be assessed independently.) It is suggested that the use of network type is relevant for other client groups and other age brackets. This broader use is potentially possible with only minor adaptations to the measurement instrument. The potential of the network instrument as a tool to create team, "patch", or neighbourhood profiles has already been recognized.

Use of the network typology as a practice tool will demand adequate training and therefore has resource implications. It has been suggested above that variation in network type should become part of the basic training of community care workers. For those already working in the community a minimum of one full days training would be needed on the introduction of the instrument, followed by a half-day follow-up session after it had been in use for several weeks.

Some social workers have commented that a service-led response results from limitations on resources and time. Awareness of needs for which there are no available solutions leads to frustration, when lack of time makes the development of more imaginative local resources impossible. If assessment of network type - or any assessment of problems/needs - is to be used imaginatively, there would need to be a paradigm shift in the thinking of policy-makers, managers and community care workers to provide time and incentives, so that case/care management would be directed towards meeting needs and solving problems rather than assigning, or increasingly rationing, existing services. This change is likely to be the most difficult of all.

The support network typology and the PANT assessment instrument represent a breakthrough in understanding how the community works. In the current context of the shift away from residential care they could become essential aids for the achievement of community based care. However, it is clear that the use of the typology in practice will only be acceptable to community care workers if it is introduced in a context of organizational security/stability; with adequate training; and, into a service which provides: (1) the resources necessary to provide elderly people who need help with supportive and preventive interventions; and, (2) community care workers with the satisfaction of delivering a quality service. Used well, it is suggested that the network typology would help care purchasers and formal care providers to determine service mix appropriate to specific sub-populations. The network typology and the distribution of support network types represent a useful new tool for community care workers, planners and policy makers to work more flexibly, to create more appropriate care packages, to predict outcomes more accurately, and to target interventions more sensitively and more cost-effectively.

Appendix A
Network Assessment Instrument

Practitioner Assessment of Network Type (P.A.N.T.)
Centre for Social Policy Research and Development,
University of Wales, Bangor.

Local Authority: _____

Name of Team: _____

Job Description (Qualified/unqualified social worker,
                community nurse etc):

_____

Date: _____

Client/Patient Information

Case No: _____ New/old (please circle)

Client's/Patient's Name: _____

Address: _____

_____

Age: _____

Gender (M/F): _____

Marital Status (M, S, W, S/D): _____

Household composition (lives alone; with spouse only; in same household
as adult child, with other elderly relative/s; other):

_____

Client's/Patient's problems/needs as identified by them: In their own words.

_____

_____

_____

_____

Client's/Patient's problems/needs as identified by practitioner:

_____

_____

_____

_____

Previous history known to interviewer

_____

_____

101

Network assessment instrument*

*This form should only be used in conjunction with the appropriate training package devised by Dr.G. Clare Wenger, Centre for Social Policy Research and Development, University of Wales, Bangor

© G. Clare Wenger

Instructions

1. Ask all questions and circle code
2. Circle same code across all boxes on same line
3. Count (do not add) circled codes for each network column and enter number at bottom of column
4. Highest number on bottom line will be in column of respondent's network type

Question	Response categories	Code	Family dependent	Locally Integrated	Local self-contained	Wider community focused	Private
1. How far away, in distance, does your nearest child or other relative live? *Do not include spouse*	No relatives	A					
	Same house/within 1 mile	B	B				
	1-5 miles	C		C			
	6-15 miles	D		D	D		
	16-50 miles	E			E	E	E
	50+ miles	F				F	F
2. If you have any children, where does your nearest child live?	No relatives	A			A		A
	Same house/within 1 mile	B	B	B			
	1-5 miles	C	C	C			
	6-15 miles	D		D	D		
	16-50 miles	E			E		
	50+ miles	F				F	F
3. If you have any living sisters or brothers, where does your nearest sister or brother live?	No sisters or brothers	A				A	A
	Same house/within 1 mile	B	B	B			
	1-5 miles	C	C	C	C		
	6-15 miles	D		D	D		
	16-50 miles	E			E		
	50+ miles	F				F	F
4. How often do you see any of your children or other relatives to speak to?	Never/no relative	A					A
	Daily	B	B	B			
	2-3 times a week	C	C	C			
	At least weekly	D			D		
	At least monthly	E			E	E	
	Less often	F				F	F
5. If you have friends in this community/neighbourhood, how often do you have a chat or do something with one of your friends?	Never/no friends	A					A
	Daily	B		B		B	
	2-3 times a week	C		C		C	
	At least weekly	D		D		D	
	At least monthly	E	E		E		
	Less often	F	F		F		F

102

Question	Response categories	Code	Family dependent	Locally integrated	Local self-contained	Wider community focused	Private
6. How often do you see any of your neighbours to have a chat with or do something with?	No contact with neighbours	A	A				A
	Daily	B		B			
	2-3 times a week	C		C			
	At least weekly	D		D	D	D	
	At least monthly	E	E		E	E	
	Less often	F	F				F
7. Do you attend any religious meetings?	Yes, regularly	A		A		A	
	Yes, occasionally	B	B		B	B	
	No	C			C		C
8. Do you attend meetings of any community/ neighbourhood or social groups, such as old people's clubs, lectures or anything like that?	Yes, regularly	A		A		A	
	Yes, occasionally	B	B		B		
	No	C	C		C		C
NETWORK TYPE (highest number)							

Information received from:	All from client/patient	1
(code as appropriate)	Some or all from proxy	2

Network type:

103

Appendix B

PANT CODING FRAME - PHASE I   CASE NO.   ☐☐☐

1 AUTHORITY: Cumbria   1
                     Coventry   2
                     Clwyd/Powys   3
                     Gwynedd   4   ☐

2 LOCAL TEAM: Egremont/Dales   1
                     Ulverston/High Furness   2
                     Coventry   3
                     Aberconwy EPH   4
                     Aberconwy Hosp. Dist.   5
                     Arfon   6
                     Llangollen   7
                     ADEPT   8
                     Llanrhaedr   9   ☐

3 INTERVIEWER: 2 initials (check)
            Except: Jenny Beard   JE
                    June Bunter   JU
                    Janet Evans   JV
                    John Hudson   JN
                    Barbara Jones   BA
                    Gareth Jones   GA
                    Sian Jones   SI
                    Joan Shaw   JA   ☐☐

4 JOB DESCRIPTION: Senior social worker   1
                     Social worker (qual.)   2
                     Social worker (unqual.) 3
                     Home care organiser/
                        community services officer 4
                     Community nurse/HV   5
                     O.T./O,T. assistant/trainee 6
                     Psychologist/CPN   7
                     Other   8
                     Missing   9   ☐

5 TYPE OF CASE: Old   1
                     New   2
                     Missing   9   ☐

105

Client information

AGE: If missing   00   ☐☐   10-11

GENDER: Male   1
             Female   2
             Couple   3
             Missing   9   ☐   12

MARITAL STATUS:
             Married/cohabiting   1
             Widowed   2
             Single   3
             S/D   4
             Missing   9   ☐   13

HOUSEHOLD COMPOSITION:

             Lives alone   1
             With spouse only   2
Could include⌈ With younger generation 3
spouse   ⌊ With same generation   4
             Foster care   5
             Residential care   6
             Other   7
             Missing   9   ☐   14

Client Identified Needs

	Circle codes		Code cols
	Yes	No	
None recorded/missing/unable to state	1	0	15
Says "None"	1	0	16
Mobility/physical health related:	1	0	17
Help with household tasks: (meals, ADL, cleaning, laundry)	1	0	18
Help with personal care: (bathing, medication, dressing, etc.)	1	0	19
Problems with sight/hearing/speech	1	0	20
Aids: bath, mobility, ADL (including wheelchairs)	1	0	21
Modification to property: (handrails, WC, shower, steps etc.)	1	0	22
Linkage help - shopping/pension/transport/phone/ getting out of house	1	0	23
Emergency help - falls, alarm systems	1	0	24
Emotional/mental health related:	1	0	25
Help related to dementia/memory/confusion etc.	1	0	26
Other mental health problems - depression, anxiety, tension, guild, paranoia etc.	1	0	27
Loneliness	1	0	28
Social contacts/ companionship/more visits	1	0	29
Relationship/marital problems	1	0	30
Emotional support/reassurance/bereavement	1	0	31
Carer related:	1	0	32
Day care	1	0	33
Respite or holiday care	1	0	34
Other carer support/relief	1	0	35
Other:			
Accommodation/housing related	1	0	36
Bizarre	1	0	37
Other/Idiosyncratic	1	0	38
Residential Care/Part III	1	0	39

107

Practitioner Identified Problems

	Yes	No	Code Cols
None/none recorded	1	0	40
Mobility/physical health related:	1	0	41
Limited mobility/disabled	1	0	42
Rheumatism/arthritis	1	0	43
Heart condition/circulation	1	0	44
Other illnesses	1	0	45
Hearing/sight problems	1	0	46
Incontinence	1	0	47
Falls	1	0	48
Pain	1	0	49
Post-operative care	1	0	50
Self-care related:	1	0	51
Inadequate nutrition/not eating	1	0	52
Poor self-care/hygiene	1	0	53
Mental health related:	1	0	54
Cognitive impairment/disorientation/confusion/ dementia/memory impairment	1	0	55
Depression/low mood	1	0	56
Anxiety/paranoia/phobias	1	0	57
Hallucinations/delusions	1	0	58
Alcohol/drug abuse	1	0	59
Recent bereavement/grief	1	0	60
Wandering/night disturbance	1	0	61
Medication/drug routine related	1	0	62
Social problems:	1	0	63
Loneliness	1	0	64
Isolation	1	0	65
Family/Carer stress	1	0	66
Friend/Neighbour stress	1	0	67
Physical abuse/violence	1	0	68
Difficult behaviour	1	0	69
Other	1	0	70
Financial/Benefits related	1	0	80

108

Practitioner Identified Needs

	Yes	No	Code Cols
None/none recorded	1	0	72
Personal care help	1	0	73
Carer relief/support/education	1	0	74
Respite care/holidays	1	0	75
Day care	1	0	76
Mobility aids	1	0	77
Modification/Repairs to home	1	0	78
Housing/accommodation help	1	0	79
Linkage help (shopping/transport/telephone/alarm)	1	0	80
Household help/ADL	1	0	1
Companionship/social contact/resocialization/stimulation	1	0	2
Supervision/monitoring	1	0	3
Residential care	1	0	4
Assessment	1	0	5
Other	1	0	6
Emotional support/counselling/advice	1	0	7

109

Previous history of:

	Yes	No	Code Cols
None recorded	1	0	8
Disabled/limited mobility/arthritis etc.	1	0	9
Stroke/haemiplegia	1	0	10
Subject to falls/falling	1	0	11
Recent surgery/hospital discharge	1	0	12
Dementia/cognitive deterioration/memory problems/ confusion etc.	1	0	13
Mental illness (incl. schizophrenia, anxiety, suicide attempts)	1	0	14
Depression/depressive illness/low mood	1	0	15
Personality change problems	1	0	16
Hostile/difficult behaviour, mood swings, verbal violence	1	0	17
Violence/physical abuse	1	0	18
Alcohol/drug abuse	1	0	19
Conflict with family/neighbours	1	0	20
Marital problems/divorce	1	0	21
Family network aged/died/unable to cope/ will not help/absent	1	0	22
Loneliness/fear of being alone	1	0	23
Social isolation/withdrawal/solitary lifestyle	1	0	24
Need for emotional support/reassurance/ dependent personality	1	0	25
Self-neglect/poor dietary intake	1	0	26
Spouse in poor health	1	0	27
Carer stress/respite care	1	0	28
Carer determined to continue	1	0	29
Early retirement	1	0	30
Independent lifestyle	1	0	31
Bereavement	1	0	32
Other	1	0	33
Social services input	1	0	34
Refused help in past	1	0	35

110

Appendix C

Network Defining Questions (%)[1]

	All	Family Depend.	Locally Integrated	Local self-cont.		Wider commun. focused		Private restric.
	(289)	(44)	(63)	(39)		(19)		(114)

Nearest child or other relative

	All	Family Depend.	Locally Integrated	Local self-cont.		Wider commun. focused		Private restric.
No relative	6	0	2	3	(1)	0		12
Within 1 mile	37	93	51	5	(2)	5	(1)	24
1-5 miles	19	7	38	21	(8)	0		14
6-15 miles	10	0	6	46	(18)	0		6
16-50 miles	8	0	3	26	(10)	26	(5)	5
50+ miles	20	0	0	0		68	(13)	39
	100	100	100	100		100		100

Nearest child

	All	Family Depend.	Locally Integrated	Local self-cont.		Wider commun. focused		Private restric.
No children	37	9	25	49	(19)	11	(2)	52
Within 1 mile	25	80	37	5	(2)	0		9
1-5 miles	11	7	25	5	(2)	0		10
6-15	6	0	8	21	(8)	0		4
16-50	5	2	2	16	(6)	16	(3)	2
50+ miles	17	2	3	5	(2)	74	(14)	25
	100	100	100	100		100		100

Nearest sibling

	All	Family Depend.	Locally Integrated	Local self-cont.		Wider commun. focused		Private restric.
No living siblings	51	36	41	36	(14)	53	(10)	69
Within 1 mile	12	36	24	3	(1)	0		2
1-5 miles	11	14	16	15	(6)	0		4
6-15 miles	7	7	13	21	(8)	0		1
16-50 miles	5	0	5	18	(7)	0		3
50+ miles	15	7	2	8	(3)	47	(9)	22
	100	100	100	100		100		100

Network Defining Questions (%)

	All	Family Depend.	Locally integrated	Local self-cont.	Wider commun. focused	Private restric.
	(289)	(44)	(63)	(39)	(19)	(114)

Frequency see any relative

	All	Family Depend.	Locally integrated	Local self-cont.	Wider commun. focused	Private restric.
Daily	28	66	46	0	0	18
2-3/week	17	34	33	10 (4)	0	7
At least weekly	13	0	13	51 (20)	5 (1)	6
At least monthly	11	0	5	33 (13)	21 (4)	9
Less often	23	0	2	5 (2)	74 (14)	42
Never/No rels.	8	0	2	0	0	18
	100	100	100	100	100	100

Frequency see/chat with friend

	All	Family Depend.	Locally integrated	Local self-cont.	Wider commun. focused	Private restric.
Daily	23	21	32	33 (13	16 (3)	16
2-3/week	22	23	33	23 (9)	37 (7)	13
At least weekly	23	21	32	23 (9)	21 (4)	17
At least monthly	7	11	0	5 (2)	26 (5)	7
Less often	4	7	0	0	0	7
Never/no friends	22	18	3	15 (6)	0	41
	100	100	100	100	100	100

Frequency see/chat to neighbours

	All	Family Depend.	Locally integrated	Local self-cont.	Wider commun. focused	Private restric.
Daily	30	21	51	26 (10)	26 (5)	25
2-3 times weekly	20	21	24	23 (9)	26 (5)	14
At least weekly	20	16	22	28 (11)	42 (8)	15
At least monthly	4	5	0	5 (2)	5 (1)	3
Less often	5	7	0	3 (1)	0	8
No contact	22	32	3	15 (6)	0	36
	100	100	100	100	100	100

	All	Family Depend.	Locally integra- ted	Local self- cont.	Wider commun. focused	Private restric.
	(289)	(44)	(63)	(39)	(19)	(114)
Attends religious meetings						
Regularly	7	5	14	3	32	3
Occasionally	7	9	11	10	16	3
Never	86	86	75	87	53	95
	100	100	100	100	100	100
Attends community/vol. org. meetings						
Regularly	30	9	70	15	79	15
Occasionally	7	7	6	15	1	3
Never	63	84	24	69	11	83
	100	100	100	100	100	100

[1]Column may not add to 100 due to rounding of percentages

References

Caldock, Kerry (1993), `Changes in Assessment: examining the relationships between recent policy and practitioners' knowledge, attitudes and practice', *Health and Social Care in the Community*, vol. 1, no. 3, pp. 139-146.

Clifford, D. (1990), *The Social Costs and Rewards of Caring*, Avebury Studies of Care in the Community, Gower Publishing, Aldershot, England.

Collins, Jean (1991), `Power and Local Community Action', *Journal of Aging Studies*, vol. 5, no 2, pp. 209-18.

Department of Health (DoH) (1989), *Caring for People: community care in the next decade and beyond* (Government White Paper). London, HMSO.

Department of Health (DoH) (1990), *Community Care in the Next Decade and Beyond: Policy Guidance*, London, HMSO.

Goldberg, E.M. (1965), `Working in the Community: what kind of help do people need?', *Social Work*, special issue on Care in the Community, April/July, pp. 6-18.

Goldberg, E.M. and Warburton, R.W. (1979), *Ends and Means in Social Work*, London, Allen and Unwin.

Griffiths, Sir Roy (1988), *Community Care: Agenda for Action - A report to the Secretary of State for Social Services*, London HMSO.

Hadley, R.; Cooper, M.; Dale, P. and Stacy, G. (1987), *A Community Social Worker's Handbook*, London, Tavistock.

Hadley, R.; Dale, P. and Sills, P. (1984). *Decentralising Social Services: A Model for Change*, London, Bedford Square Press.

Handy, C.B. (1985 third edition). *Understanding Organizations*, London, Penguin.

Hunt, A. (1978). *The Elderly at Home*, London, OPCS, HMSO.

Qureshi, H. and Walker, A. (1989). *The Caring Relationship: elderly people and their families*, London, MacMillan.

115

Seed, P. (1990). *Introducing Network Analysis in Social Work*, London, Jessica Kingsley.

Townsend, P. (1962) *The Last Refuge*, Routledge and Kegan Paul, London.

Trevellion, S. (1990). "Post Griffiths Networking: a study in contradiction", BASAPP Newsletter, Summer, pp. 12-15.

Welsh Office (1991). *Managing Care: Guidance Assessment and the Provision of Social and Community Care*, Cardiff.

Wenger, G. Clare (1984). *The Supportive Network: coping with old age*, London, Allen and Unwin.

Wenger, G. Clare (1987). *Relationships in Old Age - inside support networks*, CSPRD Report, Bangor, University of Wales.

Wenger, G. Clare (1988). *Old People's Health and Experiences of the Caring Services*, Liverpool, Liverpool University Press.

Wenger, G. Clare (1989). "Support Networks in Old Age - constructing a typology", in Margot Jefferys (Ed.) *Ageing in the 20th Century*, London, Routledge, pp. 166-85.

Wenger, G. Clare (1990). "Elderly Carers: the need for appropriate intervention", *Ageing and Society*, 10, 2, pp. 197-219.

Wenger, G. Clare (1990a). *Support Networks of Elderly People: A Guide for Practitioners*, Draft CSPRD Report.

Wenger, G. Clare (1990b). "Change and adaptation in informal support networks of elderly people in Wales 1979-87" *Journal of Aging Studies*, 4, 4, pp. 375-89.

Wenger, G. Clare (1990c). "Personal Care: variations in network type, style and capacity" in Jaber F. Gubrium and Andrea Sankar (Eds.) *The Home Care Experience: ethnography and policy*, Newbury Park, CA., Sage Publications pp. 145-72.

Wenger, G. Clare (1992). *Help in Old Age - Facing up to Change: a longitudinal network study*, Liverpool, Institute of Human Ageing, Liverpool University Press.

Wenger, G. Clare (1993). "Network Formation, Self-help, Mutual Aid and Old People in Contemporary Britain", *Journal of Aging Studies*, 7, 1, 25-40.

Wenger, G. Clare (1994). *Support Networks of Elderly People: A Guide for Practitioners*, Bangor, University of Wales.

Wenger, G. Clare and Said Shahtahmasebi (1989). *Network Variation: Demographic Correlates of Network Type* CSPRD Report, Bangor, University of Wales.

Wenger, G. Clare and Shahtahmasebi, Said (1990). "Variations in Support Networks: some policy implications" in John Mogey (Ed). *Aiding and Aging: the coming crisis*, Westport, CT.,Greenwood Press, pp. 255-77.

116

Wenger. G. Clare and Shahtahmasebi, Said (1991). "Survivors: Support Network Variation and Sources of Help in Rural Communities", *Journal of Cross-cultural Gerontology*, 6, 1, pp. 41-82.

Index